ANTIQUE BAROMETERS

Also by the author and published by Baros Books:

Barometers: Stick or Cistern Tube
Barometers: Wheel or Banjo
Barometers: Aneroid and Barographs
Visiting Cards and Cases

ANTIQUE BAROMETERS

An Illustrated Survey

Edwin Banfield

Baros Books

© Edwin Banfield 1976

First published 1976

Reprinted 1977, 1978, 1980, 1981, 1983 and 1989

British Library Cataloguing in Publication Data

Banfield, Edwin
  Antique barometers
  1. English barometers, ca 1690 – ca 1920
  I. Title
  681'.2

  ISBN 0-948382-04-X

Published by Baros Books, 5 Victoria Road, Trowbridge, Wiltshire,
England. BA14 7LH

Printed and bound in Great Britain by A. Wheaton & Co. Ltd., Exeter

CONTENTS

The barometer is one of the most valuable instruments ever contrived for investigating the nature and laws of the wonderful ocean of air in which we live.

Admiral Fitzroy 1860

Preface

I have never – and still do not – consider myself to be a writer, but as there is at present no book available on antique domestic barometers, I felt that an effort should be made to fill this obvious need. As far as I am aware, only two books have been published this century on English barometers and both have, for some years, been out of print.

This book is the result. It is written around a representative collection of barometers that I have seen or handled over a number of years. In addition to their descriptions, I have tried to collate, in an easily readable form, information on barometers obtained from a large number of sources, some of which are noted in the bibliography, giving a short history of their development.

Readers may find various errors and omissions in the text and it is possible that some of the dates attributed to the barometers will be questioned. If there is any evidence available to show that I am in error in any respect, I should appreciate being advised.

In this book I have not attempted to cover the more technical aspects of barometers or to present much in the way of new research or theories. Its main purpose is to assist the small collector and to widen the knowledge and under-standing of the barometer for the layman who possess or wishes to acquire one. It may also be of help to the antique dealer who, in the past, has hesitated to stock them because he felt he had insufficient knowledge of their workings.

Most barometers are attractive pieces of furniture that would grace any hall or living-room, and collecting them is a practical proposition as most are neither large nor heavy and require little or no attention. Unlike other furniture they take up no floor space and anyone with an eye for beauty of line and grace of proportion cannot but admire the early stick and wheel barometers.

In addition to being an object of beauty the barometer is functional and is always ready to disclose – some with a gentle tap – the likely course of the weather for the ensuing hours. A further attraction is that almost all are engraved with the maker's name and often his address so that it is possible, by a little research, to discover its approximate age and, sometimes, interesting information about the maker.

Almost all the types of barometers illustrated in this book were produced in sufficient numbers to make them available for purchase, from time to time, at auctions or in antique shops. Nearly all the barometers used as illustrations are reproduced for the first time; I have, as far as possible, avoided the familiar examples in museums which are usually illustrated and where, in any case, the original is easily accessible. I have not, except in one or two cases, shown illustrations of barometers that were made individually for a specific purpose or person.

There is a glamour about the past which has a romantic appeal, and I hope this book will stimulate interest in the antique barometer.

E. B.

To my wife and daughters

Acknowledgements

I am indebted to Negretti & Zambra Limited of Aylesbury and to the Meteorological Offices at Bracknell for their willing assistance and for allowing me access to various old catalogues and documents. Thanks are also due to Mr Ray Pitt for designing the cover and to Miss Elaine Mason for reading the manuscript.

The book would probably not have been attempted but for Miss Marian Budd who, by so readily offering to type the manuscript, issued an unintentional challenge, and to her I am extremely grateful.

1 The Experiment

It can be assumed that interest in weather forecasting began in prehistoric times when human intelligence developed to the extent that man was aware of a past and a future and appreciated that his comfort and well-being depended on a sympathetic combination of sunshine, wind and rain.

Amateur forecasting continued down the ages by studying the sun, the moon and the stars. The leaves on certain trees and berries in the hedgerows were observed, whilst the behaviour of birds and animals was carefully monitored as though they had a better knowledge of the coming weather than human beings themselves.

From these observations numerous maxims, including the following, were evolved over the centuries:

Red sky at night, shepherds delight,
Red sky in the morning, shepherds warning.

Swallows high, staying dry,
Swallows low, wet 'twill blow.

The English have always appeared to have a strange preoccupation with the weather; indeed, many foreigners would claim that the weather is the Englishman's sole topic of conversation. It is, therefore, a little ironic that the barometer was invented by a foreigner. The word 'barometer' is derived from the Greek root 'baros', meaning 'weight', and the sole purpose of a barometer is to measure the weight of the atmosphere.

The barometer was, in fact, invented by an Italian, Evangelista Torricelli, who was born in Faenza, Italy, in 1608. When he was about the age of 20 he went to the University of Rome to study under Castelli, a scientist. He became a mathematician and was influenced by the writings of the great Galilei Galileo who was the first astronomer to use the telescope for examining the sun, the moon and the stars. Galileo was responsible for the pendulum's laws, was the founder of the science of mechanics and laid the foundations of modern physics and astronomy. The two men must have become acquainted because in 1641, at the invitation of Galileo, Torricelli moved to Florence to live and work with him. Galileo was then aged 77 and completely blind; regrettably the association was shortlived as Galileo died 3 months later and Torricelli succeeded him as mathematician in the court of Tuscany.

Amongst Galileo's papers Torricelli found various notes on incompleted studies. One which interested him related to water, which, it appeared, could not be raised more than 33 feet with a single-stage suction pump. To reduce the size of the apparatus Torricelli experimented with mercury. He took a glass tube approximately 36 inches long and filled it with mercury; he then placed a finger over the open end of the tube and inserted it into a container of mercury. On removing his finger he

1

found that the tube remained full of mercury to a height of about 29 inches above the surface of the mercury in the container. Further experiments soon proved that the weight of the column of mercury was proportionate to the pressure of the air outside the tube. Thus in 1643 Torricelli discovered that the height of the mercury in the tube was dependent on the pressure of the atmosphere. This has since become known as the 'Torricellian Experiment' and the space between the mercury and the top of the tube, the 'Torricellian Vacuum'. The experiment was adapted to make the first mercury barometer in 1643. Torricelli was developing the microscope when he died of a fever in Florence in 1647 at the age of 39. It is claimed by some writers that Torricelli did not himself undertake the experiment but that it was carried out by Viviani, a close friend, at the suggestion of Torricelli, who explained to him exactly what would happen.

The Hon. Robert Boyle (1627–91) appears to have been the first person to introduce the barometer to England. He was a prolific author, writing on science, philosophy and theology. Boyle was a student in Italy during the period of the Torricellian Experiment and studied the writings of Galileo. He returned to England in 1644 with particulars of the experiment and proved that the phenomenon of Torricelli's experiment was, indeed, caused by the air, that sound was impossible in a vacuum, that air was truly necessary for life and flame and that air was permanently elastic. He developed this discovery into a quantitative relationship that volume varies inversely with pressure. This is known as 'Boyles Law'.

He developed the experiment into a practical barometer, or barascope as they were then called, by being the first to use a graduated scale to record the height of the mercury in the tube; these are now known as register plates.

Since the vacuum in the inverted tube gives no resistance, any change in atmospheric pressure varies the height of the mercury in the tube. In England the average height of the mercury column is a little under 30 inches at sea level at a temperature of 32 degrees Fahrenheit and at a latitude of about 50 degrees. Nearer the equator the mean height is greater, whilst nearer the poles it is less.

When it was discovered that the variations in the height of the mercury gave an indication as to the possible changes in the weather, an attempt was made from recorded observations to deduce the height of the mercury applicable to a particular weather condition. It was found that on fine, sunny days the mercury stood generally above 30 inches, whilst on days when the weather was changeable it was usually between 29 and 30 inches; on dull, rainy days it was often below 29 inches. Because of these conclusions it became the practice to engrave the words Fair, Changeable, Rain etc. on the register plates in addition to the height from 28 to 31 inches. These weather indications are often unreliable guides as humidity, temperature and wind direction are other important factors which determine the state of the weather. They can be looked upon as rough guides, but it is the movement, up or down, of the mercury, rather than its actual height, which foretells changes in the weather.

From 1644 the barometer was developed by scientists as an instrument mainly for the measurement of heights above sea level, and it was not until about 1675 that they were made for domestic use. The earliest were made to the order and design of scientists by clockmakers and instrument-makers, with all the metalwork heavily gilded to avoid polishing, essential with other metals, which might shake the mercury and lead to the intrusion of air bubbles into the tube.

Barometers could certainly be purchased in 1675, as in that year a Richard Legh of Lyme Hall, Cheshire, wrote to his wife while he was in London: 'The carrier will bring a long deale box that hath quicksilver in itt. Prithee command that there be great care of itt, that neither of them — the box or bottle — be stirred till I come home. Tis a device I had of Sir Jonas Moore to know the weather by.'

The early domestic barometers were of simple construction and were subsequently discarded by owners, when broken or otherwise, as more sophisticated types in attractive cases became available. It is not, therefore, surprising that none of the earliest, made prior to 1690, appear to have survived.

2 Cistern Barometers

By far the most prolific and interesting of the early domestic barometer makers was John Patrick. He was apprenticed to a joiner, William Tompson, in 1686 for 7 years, and appears to have specialised in making barometers from the time he completed his apprenticeship in 1693. He soon became accepted as the leading maker of his day, and traded from Ship Court in the Old Baily, London. He was known as the 'Torricellian Operator' and his advertisements published between 1700 and 1710 showed sketches of common, portable, marine, pendant and diagonal barometers, all of which he made and sold to the public.

Patrick also sold his barometers to watchmakers, clockmakers and other retailers. Many were unsigned and it could be that the unsigned open cistern walnut barometer shown in *Fig.* 1 was made by him. It is a fine early barometer with an oak case veneered with walnut; the edges of the frame are moulded and the scrolls above the solid walnut cistern cover are fretted. This type of scrollwork was not used in the eighteenth century, and as the twisted pillars to the hood are similar to those used on clocks around 1690, the barometer can be safely dated c. 1695. The register plates are of silvered brass and decorated with acanthus patterns with an engraved border. The weather indications are in English Roman seventeenth century italics:

Very dry	31
Settled Fair	
Fair	30
Changeable	
Rain	29
Much Rain	
Stormes	28

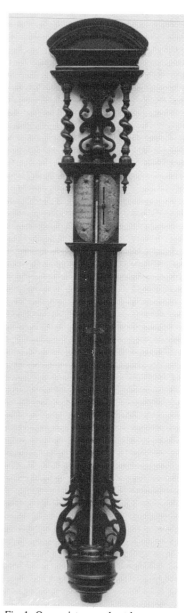

Fig. 1. Open cistern walnut barometer. Unsigned, c. 1695.

4

A sickle-shaped recording pointer is fixed in the groove on the right-hand side register plate and this has to be adjusted manually. For protection the tube is set in a deep groove down the case and is retained in position by the cistern cover, which is screwed to the frame, and the fretted brass loop screwed to the centre of the case. A wedge-shaped section of the moulded cornice below the register plates can be lifted out to allow the tube to be removed. The overall height is 47 inches and the open cistern tube was as illustrated in *Fig.* 2. A similar barometer can be seen at Hampton Court Palace, but it is fitted with a portable screw cistern tube and is dated c. 1705. It has adjustable register plates and two ball finials, but there is no decorative hood above the register plates. Other similar barometers of this William and Mary period show the Dutch marquetry influence with the cases inlaid with flowers and shell motifs, whilst some were embellished with ormolu mounts.

The main disadvantage of the open cistern tube barometer was the difficulty in moving it from place to place. Unless it was carried very carefully in an upright position, the mercury in the glass cistern could easily be spilt and this could allow air to enter the tube and so distort the reading. The air would gradually rise to the top of the mercury and enter the vacuum which would, again, give a false reading. Another hazard was that if the tube was quickly inclined away from the vertical, the mercury would rise to the top of the tube with such force that it could break the glass.

Several makers gave thought to this problem and various remedies were tried. By constricting the bore of the top inch or so of the tube the upward surge of the mercury could be contained and so prevent breakages. It was also possible to prevent the mercury being spilt by covering the open cistern with leather firmly fixed from the brim across to the tube.

These refinements did not make the barometer really portable, and there is considerable doubt as to whether John Patrick or Daniel Quare made the first truly portable barometer. The benefit of the doubt must be given to Daniel Quare because he was able to satisfy the Patent Office, who granted him a patent on 2 August 1695 giving protection to 'a portable weather glass or barometer, which may be removed and carried to any place though turned upside-down without spilling one drop of the quicksilver or letting any air into the tube, and that nevertheless the air shall have the same liberty to operate upon it as on those common ones now in use with respect to atmosphere'.

The Clockmakers' Company, of which Quare was a member, opposed the granting of the patent as it was against the exclusive possession of a trading right, and resolved to defend any member of the Company – or John Patrick who was not a member, but assisted the Company – if suits of law were brought against them for making portable barometers. However, the patent was granted and no litigation appears to have ensued, although Quare's cistern was soon imitated and improved.

The patent details gave no specification of the Quare portable barometer, but this can be established by examining his early barometers, many of which still survive. He made use of the fact that air could permeate leather and substituted the glass cistern for a leather bag, the top of which he cemented to the glass tube, thus forming a closed cistern. The leather bag was housed in a cistern box with the base of the bag resting on a padded screw, which operated through a nut set in the bottom of the cistern box. When the screw was advanced it raised the leather bag

5

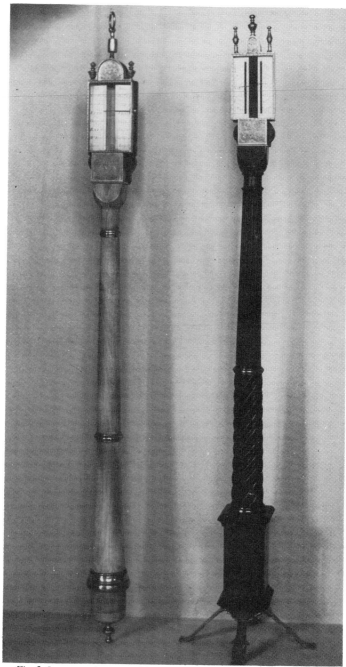

Fig. 2. Open cistern tube.

Fig. 3. Ivory pendant portable barometer by Daniel Quare, c.1710.(Reproduced by kind permission of the Curator of the City of Gloucester Museum.)

Fig. 4. Walnut pillar portable barometer. Unsigned, c. 1710. (Reproduced by kind permission of the Curator of the City of Gloucester Museum.)

and reduced the volume of the cistern until the cistern and tube were full of mercury. The barometer could then be turned upside down and carried at will, without adverse effect. When transferred to its new position it could easily be set up for operation again by withdrawing the screw to its original position.

Quare, who was born in 1649, was a Quaker and became one of the outstanding watch and clockmakers of all time. He invented the repeating watch and was Master of the Clockmakers' Company in 1708. He died in 1724. He made basically two types of portable cistern tube barometer and both are illustrated. *Fig.* 3 shows an ivory-cased portable pendant barometer by Daniel Quare made early in the eighteenth century, whilst *Fig.* 4 illustrates an unnamed pillar portable barometer in walnut made about 1710. The style is typical of the work of Quare and it could have been made by John Patrick for Quare under the patent already mentioned.

Both types of barometer are similar in many respects and have the same general appearance, except that one was made to hang on a wall whilst the other was fitted with four feet so that it could be freestanding. The feet are of brass and are hinged so that they can be retracted to hang downwards if it is desired to suspend the barometer on a wall. The pillar type usually have squared cistern covers and if the case is of walnut the lower section is usually twisted, with the upper half fluted and reeded. The register plates are of silvered brass and enclosed in a gilt brass box with a glass front. The large central finial often contains the top of the tube and the knobs on the top of the two smaller finials operate a mechanism to adjust the two recording pointers set in grooves on the register plates.

Some of Quare's barometers have register plates on two sides of the hood; one set of weather indications being in English and the other usually in French. The second set was incorporated so that the barometers could be exported to France, and to allow the choice of register plate the hood could be reversed so that either plate could face the front. The hoods were invariably exquisitely engraved with leaf motifs, as was a plate below the hood which usually bore the maker's name, as in *Fig.* 3: 'Daniel Quare, Londini Invent & Fecit'. Similar barometers can be seen in the Science Museum, London, and the Victoria and Albert Museum, London.

From this period most cistern barometers were fitted with some sort of device which made them reasonably portable, and improvements continued to be made. It was found that boxwood was pervious to air and suitable to form a closed cistern. The top of a hollow cylinder of boxwood was cemented to within an inch of the bottom of the tube, whilst the bottom of the cylinder was covered by a shallow leather bag which, again, rested on a padded adjustable screw. By adjusting the screw the barometer could be set at the correct reading by comparison with other barometers; it could also be made portable by the action of the screw raising the leather base until the cistern and tube were full of mercury.

The demand for domestic barometers grew steadily during the eighteenth century and they were made increasingly by spectaclemakers and makers of scientific instruments. However, it was the clockmakers who continued to make the more attractive barometers by producing them in ornamental and embellished cases. Notable makers of cistern barometers of high quality in the first half of the eighteenth century were Daniel Delander (1674–1744), James Ayscough (c. 1740), John Cuff (1708–1772), Thomas Heath (c. 1730) and Edward Scarlett (1688–1743).

During the first quarter of the eighteenth century there was little change in the design of barometer cases and they followed, in general, the lines of the one illustrated in *Fig.* 1, except that the hoods were shorter in length and the carved or fretted scrollwork wings above the cistern cover were no longer applied. The cases continued to be of walnut, often veneered on an oak base, until the 1730s, when walnut was replaced by mahogany which then began to be imported into the United Kingdom.

Not all the barometers during this period were of good quality and it appears that a large number of inferior specimens were made by entrepreneurs who exploited the quickly expanding market for domestic weather-glasses at this time. This prompted Edward Saul, when writing of barometers in 1730, to complain:

> As for such weather-glasses as have been lately hawked about the country by needy foreigners or peddling philosophers . . . they are generally speaking very great cheats and impositions upon those, who for sake of the meanness of the price, are persuaded to buy them: the cavity of the tube in many of them scarce large enough to receive an ordinary pin.

No doubt the makers used tubes and cisterns of small diameter to save mercury, which caused the readings to be inaccurate, and fitted them in plain cases to save expense; it is, therefore, not surprising that none appear to have survived.

From 1740 the frames were generally made of, or veneered with, mahogany, with the design following that of contemporary furniture, although clock-case designs were still favoured by the clockmakers. The influence of Chippendale can also be seen, with some high-quality cases being wide and lavishly carved in the rococo manner. By the middle of the eighteenth century an increasing number of barometers were being exported and industrial methods were being used to produce them. Division of labour was in being, with glassblowers making the tubes, engravers making the register plates and cabinet makers producing the cases; the assembly was undertaken by opticians, instrument makers and clockmakers.

Although the vast majority of the early barometers were made in London, quite a number were produced in the country, mainly by the local clockmakers. *Fig.* 5 shows an example of a country-made cistern barometer by James Verrier of North Curry in Somerset (c. 1750). He was a long-case clockmaker who appears to have developed a type of clock movement powered by barometric or temperature change. It was described in a letter to the *Western Flying Post* in 1755 as follows:

> Sir,
> I flatter myself the following description of a new invented clock which I have seen at North Curry made by James Verrier of that place, which will be acceptable to many of your readers if you please to give it place in your Weekly Mercury you will oblige, Sir, your constant reader.
>   W. B. Bridgewater 26th July

> This clock I take to be the nearest to perpetual motion of anything yet discovered, as it requires no manual assistance whatever, either to wind it up or to keep it in motion, although it sometimes descends and sometimes ascends according to the different direction of the barrel, without rachet or click, the first wheel being fixed to the barrel it shows apparent time. In this

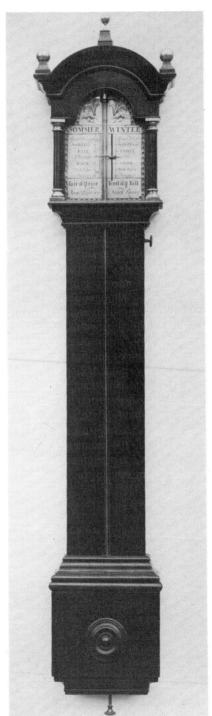

Fig. 5. Mahogany cistern barometer by James Verrier, North Curry, c. 1750.

state it was first put in motion in 1752 but the inventor knowing it to be liable to the same variations which always attend clocks has endeavoured to prevent the same, which in 1754 he thus effected by being corrected to less than a minute by influence of the sun. Upon the whole it will continue to keep in motion as long as the materials will last, foulness only excepted. It is needless to mention what advantages these clocks must be to the publick, either in towns, churches or houses. The inventor on proper encouragement is willing to exhibit a plan of the same. The machine has had the approbation of many curious persons who have seen it.

The Verrier barometer is veneered with mahogany and has the general appearance of a long-case clock. The tube is set in a deep groove and the silvered brass register plates are protected by glass, but as there is no door the sickle-shaped set pointer is moved by a rack-and-pinion mechanism which is controlled by the knob on the right-hand side of the case just below the hood. The three ball finials above the arched cornice are of brass, as are the bases and capitals of the pillars supporting the hood. The register plates are of particular interest and are shown in *Fig.* 6. The weather indications for summer and winter are given and the words are similar to those used generally up until the middle of the eighteenth century. Roman lettering with capitals and lower case is used with copperplate script. The scale is very unusual in that it only extends from 27·7 inches to 30·4 inches whilst Changeable is engraved against 29 inches, which is strange as invariably it is engraved against 29·5 inches. It could hardly be a mistake and a possible explanation is that the barometer was made at the request of a customer who lived 500 feet or so above sea level.

Fig. 6. Detail of *Fig.* 5.

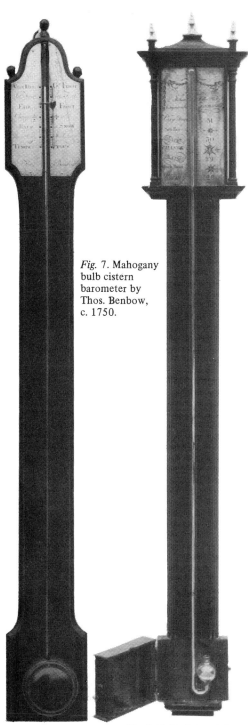

Fig. 7. Mahogany
bulb cistern
barometer by
Thos. Benbow,
c. 1750.

Fig. 8. Bulb cistern tube.

Fig. 7 shows a bulb cistern or bottle barometer of the same period by Thos. Benbow. This simple type of bulb cistern or bottle tube is shown in *Fig.* 8. Its main advantages were its ease and cheapness of construction; the disadvantages were that it was not so readily portable as the cistern type and there was no successful way of determining the scale zero. The only way to adjust the height of the mercury in the tube was to raise or lower the register plates or, alternatively, add to, or take away, mercury from the bulb cistern. Although this type of barometer never became very popular in England, it was made in very large numbers on the Continent, particularly in Holland.

The case of the Benbow barometer is of solid mahogany, as are the three ball finials. Two wire loops contain the tube and the cistern cover is held in position by pressing into the case two headless nails fixed into the cover. The register plates are of silvered brass and the summer and winter weather indications are as shown in *Fig.* 6, except that Stormy and Tempest are replaced by Tempestous. The scale extends to 3 inches with the half inches highlighted with large dots, but there are no numerals. The manually operated set pointer slides along a metal rod, raised above the plates, and is fixed in position by a screw.

The date the barometer was made is debatable, as unfortunately Thos. Benbow, unlike James Verrier, did not engrave his address on the plates, making it difficult to trace him. The form of engraving and weather indications used suggest that it could have been made before 1750, but the possibility is that Benbow was a country maker and copied the style at a later date. A clock and watchmaker named Thomas Benbow was operating in Newport, Shropshire, between 1778 and 1800, but as the barometer was found in Ireland it is doubtful whether there is any connection. The name of the maker is below the weather indications and this

suggests that it was made around the middle of the eighteenth century or earlier, when it was the common practice to engrave the name in this position. Later barometers usually have the name engraved above the scale.

Until the middle of the eighteenth century the makers satisfied themselves as to the accuracy of their barometers by ensuring that wide cisterns were used. It will be appreciated that if the diameter of the cistern is very many times greater than the diameter of the mercury in the tube, then the change in the cistern level of the mercury will be negligible when the mercury in the tube moves between 28 and 31 inches. However, in order to be able to take a more accurate reading from the scale, a vernier was often fitted to cistern tube barometers from around 1750.

The vernier was invented around 1630 by Pierre Vernier of Ornans in Burgundy, and one is fitted to the register plates of the barometer shown in *Figs.* 9 and 10. The barometer scales are usually divided into inches and tenths of an inch, whilst the vernier is one and one-tenth inches long and divided into ten equal parts numbered one to ten. The vernier scale is made to pass along the fixed barometer scale by a sliding or rack-and-pinion movement. If the first line on the vernier is in line with a one-tenth division on the scale, then the second line on the vernier will be out of line with the next one-tenth division by one-hundredth of an inch. It follows that if the first line on the vernier is out of line with any division on the scale, the correct reading can be obtained by seeing which vernier line coincides with a division on the scale. By setting the vernier zero pointer to the level of the mercury and reading the scale in conjunction with the vernier scale, an accuracy of up to one-hundredth of an inch can be achieved.

Fig. 9 illustrates an open cistern walnut and mahogany barometer made by John Bird about 1760. Bird was born in 1709 and was an optical and mathematical instrument maker in Durham until he moved to London in 1740 and worked for George Graham and Jonathan Sisson. It is not known exactly when he acquired his own workshop in the Strand, but by 1744 he had made a barometer for the meteorological station of Roger Pickering, who described it as follows:

Fig. 10. Detail of *Fig.* 9.

13

I have found those with open cisterns more sensible than the portable ones. That with which I make my observations, is with an open cistern, furnished with micrometer (vernier) that divides an inch into 400 parts; by which I am capable of perceiving the most minute alteration of the gravity of the air; it was made by Mr. Bird of the Strand, whose accuracy in graduation deserves, I think, notice and encouragement.

John Bird was a well-known maker of barometers, thermometers and astronomical instruments and was renowned for his accurate scales. His barometer shown in *Fig.* 9 has an overall height of 44 inches, whilst the hemispherical cistern cover has a width of 5 inches and is more than 3 inches in depth. The case is of oak veneered with mahogany whilst the cistern cover, ball finials and part of the hood are of solid walnut. The switch from walnut to mahogany was forced on cabinet makers soon after 1720 when the French authorities placed a ban on the export of timber, arising from a shortage of walnut wood in France. An alternative wood was mahogany which could be imported from Cuba, Puerto Rica and San Domingo, and it began to supersede walnut for making furniture during the second quarter of the century. By 1760 the use of walnut had practically ceased as the dark reddish colour of mahogany was much preferred; it was also found to be very strong, did not crack or warp and was not liable to attack from woodworm.

The vernier is operated manually within a groove on the register plates; these have weather indications which became standard around this time, and have been used ever since. The tube is of particular interest as it was widened to a bulb at the top with a diameter of approximately 2 inches. The bulb, protected by a brass cap, was designed to dilute the effect of any air or vapour that might, in time, percolate into the vacuum. This type of tube was also used by John Bennett, Jesse Ramsden, Jeremiah Sisson and John Troughton, who were all important makers and contemporaries of Bird. Examples can be seen in the Science Museum, London, and the Oxford University History of Science Museum. Also in the latter museum is a very plain barometer – or scientific instrument – made by John Bird on the same principle as the one described, except that there is an ivory float in conjunction with a portable cistern, so that the exact level of the mercury in the cistern can be established.

It should be mentioned here that thermometers were occasionally fitted to early barometers. Those made during the first half of the eighteenth century would have thermometers with the Royal Society scale or one of three Fahrenheit scales. The Royal Society scale was used during the first quarter of the eighteenth century and the sealed alcohol thermometer was calibrated from 0° 'Extream Hot' down to 90° 'Extream Cold', the opposite of that expected. The Fahrenheit scales were devised by G. D. Fahrenheit (1689–1736), a German scientist, as follows:

1st	[1710]	90°	Blood heat
	Alcohol	0°	Temperate
		–90°	Freezing point of mixture of salt, water and ice
2nd	[1717]	90°	Blood heat
	Mercury	0°	Freezing point of mixture of salt, water and ice

14

3rd	[1724]	96°	Blood heat
	Mercury or	32°	Freezing point of water
	Alcohol	0°	Freezing point of mixture of salt, water and ice

All these scales were used on thermometers fitted to barometers, but only the third scale was used after the middle of the eighteenth century.

Another refinement began to appear on some barometers around 1760; this was a hygroscope or hygrometer, which was used to determine the humidity of the air. The barometer reading is affected by a change in wind as well as by rain and one objection raised against the simple barometer was that the owner was in doubt, when the mercury level was falling, whether to expect rain or wind. The addition of a hygrometer, indicating the degree of dampness or dryness of the air, removed this doubt.

Dr Robert Hooke appears to have made the first hygrometer in England, as on 7 December 1663 he read a paper to the Royal Society on his 'Weather Observations' which included the following: 'For ascertaining . . . the moisture and dryness of the air with the degree of it . . . this is to be observed with a good hygroscope, which may be had either with the beard of an oat, a gut string or the like.' In June 1666 he recommended the 'cod of a vetch' as a substitute for a single beard of wild oat.

A hygrometer is shown above the tube of the barometer in *Fig*. 11. Its diameter is approximately 3 inches and the words Dry and Moist are engraved to the left and right, respectively, of the centre. Each side is calibrated from 0 to 30 to show the degree of dryness or moisture above or below the norm. An oat beard is fixed to the centre of the dial and glued to the top of the beard is an indicating length of straw. The beard is in the shape of a coil and the free end attached to the straw will unwind when it is moistened. The beard has only a limited effective life and very few hygrometers of this type will be found to be in working order. Except for the wet and dry bulb hygrometers, fixed to Farmers barometers in the second half of the nineteenth century and described later, the oat beard was the only type of hygrometer in general use on barometers. Its design hardly varied for 100 years other than, about 1800, the replacement of the words Dry and Moist by Dry and Damp.

The mahogany cistern barometer by Henry Pyefinch shown in *Fig*. 11 incorporates a thermometer, a vernier and a hygrometer. It was made c. 1760 and the unbroken pediment was obviously copied from the pediments surmounting the cornices of bookcases, cupboards and cabinets which were popular between 1675 and 1760. The reeding of the lower half of the hemispherical cistern cover is also typical of the same period. The Fahrenheit mercury thermometer is unusual in that the scale extends from $-30°$ to $212°$ and there are an unusual number of temperature indications engraved on the scale: $32°-$ Freezing; $55°-$ Temperate; $76°-$ Summer Heat; $98°-$ Blood Heat; $112°-$ Fever Heat; $144°-$ Melt Wax; $176°-$ Spirits Boil; $212°-$ Water Boils.

The weather indications are standard except that Inclined to Fair is used instead of Fair and Inclined to Rain is substituted for Rain.

A bayonet-type tube appears to have been introduced about the middle of the eighteenth century and one is illustrated in *Fig*. 12. By bending the tube just below the register plates it allows the lower part of the tube to be easily enclosed within

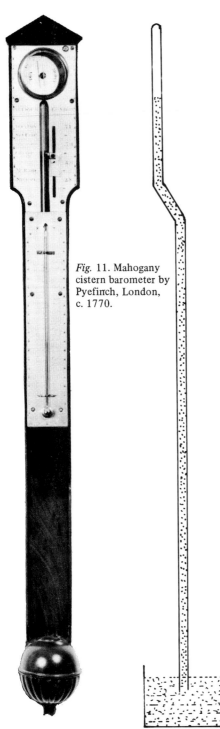

Fig. 11. Mahogany
cistern barometer by
Pyefinch, London,
c. 1770.

Fig. 12. Bayonet
cistern tube.

a panelled case. Pyefinch favoured this type of tube, possibly because it allowed him to adorn the fronts of his cases with the very delicately engraved register plates and thermometer scales for which he was noted. Such a tube was used in the barometer described, it being of the portable cistern type, but the adjusting screw is missing.

In the Victoria and Albert Museum, London, there is a similar type of barometer by Pyefinch on view. It is of a very high quality with the hood, case and cistern cover elegantly carved; it has a broken pediment with a large urn-shaped finial and the thermometer scale extends from the register plates to the cistern cover.

Henry Pyefinch traded from 67 Cornhill, London, between 1739 and 1790 and was well known as an optical and mathematical instrument maker. In 1765, in conjunction with J. H. de Magalhaens, a Portuguese scientist, he patented an instrument to measure the effect of the weight of the atmosphere and the variations caused by heat and cold.

Barometers made during the second half of the eighteenth century tended to be plainer, with less decoration to the frame; the engraving on the register plates and thermometer scales was less ornamental and these trends were, no doubt, brought about by the need, for the purposes of economy, to standardise many of the component parts. The trunk of the barometer became narrower and the influence of the long-case clock design disappeared. The structure of the cornice was more or less standardised by the introduction of the broken pediment which decorated the majority of barometers between 1780 and 1800. This type of pediment had been surmounting the cornices of bookcases and cabinets since 1715.

Fig. 13 shows a typical example of the type of common cistern barometer on

sale in 1780. It was made by Peter Dollond, a London maker, whose father, John Dollond, was a Huguenot silk weaver who fled from France in 1685. Peter started in business as an optician in 1750 and, in partnership with other members of the family, he became a notable and prolific optical instrument and barometer maker. (A nephew, George Dollond, also made barometers signed 'Dollond, London' during the first half of the nineteenth century.)

In design this barometer is much narrower and generally more slender than earlier barometers, and for this reason the type became known as stick barometers. The plain mahogany veneered case, hemispherical cistern cover, unadorned register plates and vernier are all representative of this period. The unusual spherical shaped finial is often seen on barometers by Dollond. Under the silvered brass register plates there is still a piece of paper with the scale divisions and weather indications carefully marked. This was, no doubt, prepared by Dollond and passed to the engraver who inscribed the plates.

Fig. 14 shows an interesting cistern tube mahogany barometer which was also made about 1780. It is similar in appearance to the Dollond barometer, with a broken pediment and hemispherical cistern cover, but in addition it has an alcohol thermometer mounted on the register plates and a 'Perpetual Almanack' is incorporated between the cornice and the plates (*See* detail in *Fig.* 15). The days of the month are fixed, but the days of the week can be adjusted up or down by a rack-and-pinion mechanism so that, at the beginning of each month, the days of the week can be set against the appropriate days of the month. A similar mechanism is used to allow each month to appear in turn with the days in that particular month.

It is reasonable to assume that this barometer was made by Francis Watkins,

Fig. 13. Mahogany cistern barometer by Dolland, London, c. 1780.

Fig. 14. Mahogany calendar barometer by Watkins, London, c. 1780.

17

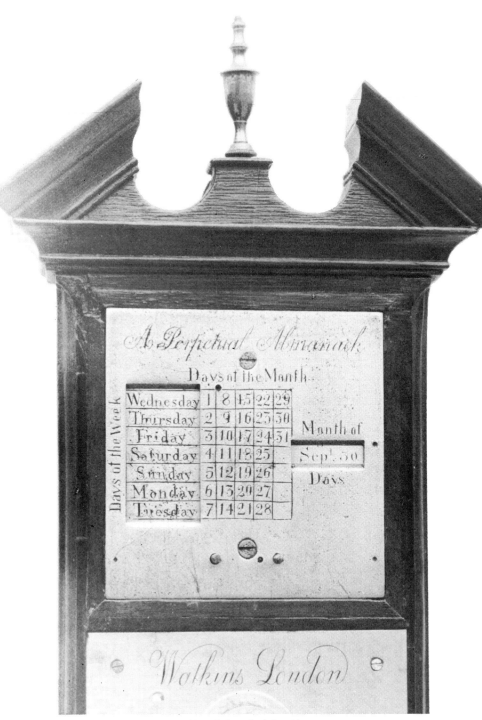

Fig. 15. Detail of *Fig.* 14.

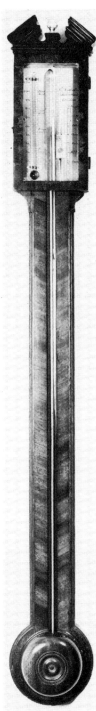

who operated from 5 Charing Cross, London, between 1747 and 1784. He became a well-known instrument maker and started a business which, by subsequent amalgamations and takeovers, today forms part of the G. E. C.-Elliott Automation Group. Watkins was best known for a type of angle barometer which included a 'Perpetual Regulation of Time'. Besides a perpetual almanack similar to the one described above, it incorporated movable dials to show the signs of the zodiac, the length of the day, the times of sunrise and sunset and the time of high water at London Bridge. One such barometer by Francis Watkins can be seen in the History of Science Museum, Oxford University, whilst a similar one by Watkins & Smith is exhibited in the Science Museum, London. (Watkins & Smith was a partnership between Francis Watkins and his former apprentice, Addison Smith.)

Towards the end of the eighteenth century it became common practice to protect the register plates with glass; this usually took the form of a hinged glazed door which could be opened by a brass knob so that the vernier could be adjusted manually before taking a reading. The glass also gave protection to the thermometer which was usually mounted on the left-hand register plate. Also during this period the turned cistern covers became more shallow and were often inlaid with a darker wood or ivory rings.

These features appear on the barometer by Baptis Roncheti illustrated in *Fig.* 16. The mahogany veneered case is outlined with zebra stringing and the panelled trunk is decorated with marquetry flower patterns. The Dry/ Moist hygrometer is adjusted by the key below the dial which operates a cog mechanism; the key is removable and can be used to adjust the screw to the portable cistern. Baptis Roncheti, one of the early Italian immigrants who settled in Manchester towards the end of the

g. 16. Mahogany stern barometer by apt. Roncheti, c, 1795.

Fig. 17. Mahogany bulb cistern barometer by C. Tagliabue, c. 1830.

19

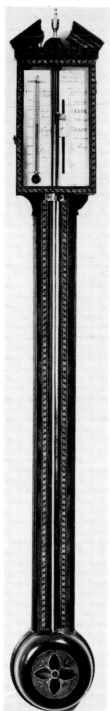

eighteenth century, was a prolific producer of high-quality barometers, which included wheel, angle and double barometers (q.v.).

During the first half of the nineteenth century a very large number of barometers were made with a broken pediment superstructure: a typical example is shown in *Fig.* 17. The frame is veneered with mahogany giving a herring-bone pattern with stringing of a lighter wood at the edges. The shallow turned cistern cover protects the bulb cistern tube and the hinged and glazed door protects the register plates and Fahrenheit alcohol thermometer.

The barometer was made by Ceasar Tagliabue, who was an optician and barometer maker. He traded from various addresses in London between 1807 and 1846; the address engraved on the register plates is '23, Hatton Gdn., London', where he was operating from 1829 to 1847. In 1837 his eldest daughter married his apprentice, Louis Casella, whom he took into partnership in 1838. The firm flourished and still trades today as scientific instrument makers under the name of C. F. Casella & Co. Ltd. Louis Casella was the maker of the agricultural barometer shown in *Fig.* 92.

Another broken-pediment stick barometer of the same period is shown in *Fig.* 18. It is of exceptional quality. The case is again veneered with mahogany, to give a herring-bone pattern, and for additional adornment there is ebony and boxwood stringing which borders an intricate chequered inlay. The same design is used on the glazed door whilst the shallow turned cistern cover is inlayed with different coloured woods to form leaves and flower head. The engraved silvered register plates have the standard weather indications and the vernier is operated manually. A Fahrenheit alcohol thermometer is used and the scale shows the following four common heat

Fig. 18. Mahogany bulb cistern barometer by C. Aiano, c. 1830.

Fig. 19. Mahogany cistern barometer by Blunt, London, c. 1805.

20

indications: Blood Heat, Summer Heat, Temperate and Freezing. The maker's name 'Charles Aiano, North Gate, Canterbury' is engraved on the register plates. He. was a maker of clocks, barometers and thermometers and an optician working at North Gate between 1828 and 1841.

Although the majority of stick barometers made during this period were of the broken-pediment type, there were numerous other designs produced by various makers, which should be mentioned.

An important maker was Thomas Blunt, who produced a large number of barometers very similar to the one illustrated in *Fig.* 19. The round-topped case is a feature of this barometer. It is veneered with mahogany in the herring-bone style with an edging of ebonised veneer. This type of ebonised veneer was often used by cabinet makers after the death of Nelson in 1805, and it is suggested that it was introduced as a mark of respect for him. The portable cistern is protected by an egg-shaped cover which Blunt favoured and used almost exclusively. Blunt traded from 22 Cornhill, London, from 1760 to 1822. He was apprenticed to Edward Nairne in 1760 and was taken into partnership in 1774. The partnership lasted until the death of Nairne in 1806, but it appears that whilst in partnership both Nairne and Blunt continued their own individual businesses using their sole names.

Blunt was a mathematical and optical instrument maker of repute; he designed some of the features of the 'New Barometer' of the Portuguese scientist J. H. de Magellan, and became, 'Mathematical Instrument Maker to his Majesty the King'. His trade card advertised telescopes for sea and land, sextants, Hadley's quadrants, marine barometers, azimuth and other compasses, spectacles and reading glasses, opera glasses, theodolites and other surveying instruments, microscopes, globes, thermometers, electrical machines, sun dials, cases of drawing instruments, rules, pencils etc. etc.

The design of the round-top barometer cases was taken from the round-top bookcases and china cabinets which were in vogue during the Sheraton period around 1790. The simple rounded top was often used on barometers by the beginning of the nineteenth century and persisted, in one form or another, right through the century.

Another common feature which appeared at about the same time was the scroll pediment, used on the barometer shown in *Fig.* 20. It is also called a swan-necked pediment and was copied from the pediments that surmounted the cornices of bureau–bookcases and china cabinets of the Chippendale, Hepplewhite and Sheraton periods. This type of pediment became popular and was incorporated in many different barometer designs during the first half of the nineteenth century. The circular section at the top of the scroll or swan neck is sometimes decorated with carved ivory rosettes.

The barometer was made by Jones of 241, Oxford Street, London, about 1810 and the design is representative of the period. The pine case is veneered with mahogany and outlined with ebonised stringing which extends round the glazed register plate cover and cistern cover. The portable cistern tube is protected by a panelled case and shallow turned cistern cover. The thermometer case is fixed and the circular key below the register plates is used to adjust the vernier. A key is necessary as the glass protecting the plates is fixed. The glass can only be removed by detaching the complete cornice and pediment section and then sliding the glass upwards.

Another type of round-top pediment used during the second quarter of the

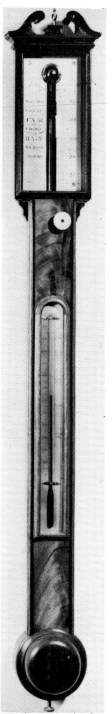

nineteenth century is shown in *Fig.* 21. The case is of solid mahogany as is the flat turned cistern cover. As the case is not panelled, the mercury thermometer is mounted on the silvered register plates. The thermometer is interesting because, in addition to the Fahrenheit scale, it has the Reaumur scale. In 1730 Rene A. F. de Reaumur suggested a scale with a freezing point of zero and a boiling point at 80°. The scale was adopted and named after him; it was used extensively on the continent, but is not often seen in the United Kingdom. The scale appears to have been used with thermometers attached to barometers from the beginning of the nineteenth century, but always as an addition to the Fahrenheit scale. The glass protecting the register plates is fixed, making it necessary to use a key to adjust the vernier. The barometer, which can be dated c. 1825, was made by H. Hughes of 120 Fenchurch Street, London.

The vast majority of barometers made during the eighteenth century had silvered brass register plates, but occasionally the register plates were printed on paper. They were sometimes favoured by country makers, but were not used on any particular design until the nineteenth century when paper plates were the rule on barometers of the design illustrated in *Fig.* 22.

This design was popular with some of the early Italian makers and was copied by a few English makers. The veneered mahogany case has a shallow hinged box to house the bulb cistern and the tube is held in place by wire threaded through from the back of the case. The pillared hood is a reminder of earlier clockcase designs whilst the pagoda type pediment suggests the Chinese Chippendale influence of 1765—70. The finials are of brass. The scale and standard weather indications are printed on paper and decorated with two flying cherubs trailing garlands of leaves. The plates are protected by glass which is fixed flush

Fig. 20. Mahogany cistern barometer by Jones, London, c. 1810.

Fig. 21. Mahogany cistern barometer by H. Hughes, London, c. 1825.

22

against them. The maker was Matthew Woller of 51, Edgbaston Street, Birmingham, who made clocks and barometers from that address between 1801 and 1808. His name and address are printed on the plates, as are the words 'Warranted Good'. A very similar barometer by Dominick Manticha can be seen in the Science Museum, London.

One other type of barometer which was invariably made with paper plates is shown in *Fig.* 23. The oak case is veneered with mahogany and the hemispherical bulb cistern cover is in two sections – an upper and a lower half – which suggests that this type of barometer may originally have been fitted with an open cistern tube. This type of instrument, which features paper plates and a simple arched case, was common on the Continent from early in the eighteenth century, but it did not become popular in England until the end of the century. The printed plates are decorated with a leaf and fruit patterned border and are protected with glass which is fixed flush against the plates. The maker was Adam Routledge of Carlisle, an early nineteenth century watch, clock and barometer maker. The collection of barometers in the Gloucester Museum includes one of this type by Houghton of Farnworth, near Warrington.

During the second quarter of the nineteenth century the broken and scroll or swan-neck pediment barometers became less popular and were displaced, in the main, by barometers with round tops or square moulded tops. Also at this time the silvered brass register plates and thermometer scales were superseded, over a period, by ivory register plates and thermometer scales.

Fig. 24 shows an example of a popular type of stick barometer made between 1815 and 1830. The case is of solid mahogany and is bow-fronted so that the attractive grain in the wood can be highlighted. The ebonised urn-shaped cistern

Fig. 22. Mahogany bulb cistern barometer by Mathew Woller, c. 1805.

Fig. 23. Mahogany bulb cistern barometer by Adam Routledge, c. 1820.

23

Fig. 24. Mahogany cistern barometer by Wm.Holmes, London, c. 1820.

Fig. 25. Detail of *Fig.* 24.

Fig. 26. Ordinary mahogany barometer, c. 1820.

Fig. 27. Satinwood cistern barometer by Gardners, Glasgow, c. 1822.

cover was probably copied from the urn shapes which decorated sideboards during the Robert Adam and Hepplewhite furniture periods. There is matching ebonised stringing applied to the edges of the case and the mercury thermometer has an ivory plate engraved with both Fahrenheit and Reaumur scales. The thermometer has a fixed bow-fronted glass case and this design is repeated to form the hood. The only way of removing the bow glass protecting the ivory register plates is to remove the square moulded top, making it necessary to fix an ivory key below the hood to adjust the vernier by a rack-and-pinion mechanism. The key is detachable and is also used to turn the screw to the portable cistern. There are only three weather indications, Fair, Change and Rain, which is common for this type of barometer.

The barometer was made by William Holmes, who was also an important clockmaker; he had a workshop at Somerset House, Strand, London, between 1802 and 1824, and was the son of John Holmes, a clockmaker of great repute who, in 1779, supervised the making, by Thwaites, of the clock for Greenwich Hospital.

The register plates of the William Holmes barometer are shown in detail in *Fig.* 25 so that the changes in the style of engraving which took place during the Regency period can be seen. *Figs.* 6 and 10 illustrate the style of lettering applied to eighteenth century barometers, which consisted of Roman capitals and lower case, Roman upper and lower case italics or joined copperplate script. Pronounced serifs were often applied to the capital letters. A gradual change to a gothic style of lettering took place during the first quarter of the nineteenth century, with Change being engraved as shown in *Fig.* 25. Broad Roman serif capitals, as shown, were used for Fair and Rain, but the previously applied Roman capitals and lower case continued to be used for the rest of the register plate lettering. By the third quarter of the nineteenth century Roman sanserif capitals were being used as illustrated in *Fig.*44 (p. 46).

In complete contrast to the elegant William Holmes barometer, an inexpensive ordinary barometer is shown in *Fig.* 26. The plain mahogany case is grooved to contain the tube which is held in place by a tapered rectangle of wood which slots into position below the centre of the case. The indicator housing is of brass, but the register plate is made of glazed cardboard. The tube has the same bore throughout its length so that a rise of half an inch in the mercury is shown as a rise of 1 inch on the scale, which is calibrated from 28 to 31 inches with divisions of one-tenth of an inch.

The hanging ring has a hand-made screw, which suggests that the barometer was made prior to 1851, whilst the indicator housing appears to be of late Georgian design. The initials T. N. P. are punched on the side of the case and these are, no doubt, the maker's.

The barometers so far described have all been made of walnut or mahogany. Walnut was used exclusively until about 1730; then mahogany became popular and was in general use until around 1780, when satinwood was occasionally used for making barometers of particularly high quality. However, mahogany remained by far the most popular wood for barometer cases until about 1840, when rosewood was often offered as an alternative.

An example of a cistern barometer in a satinwood case is shown in *Fig.* 27. The satinwood gives the effect of crossbanding between the moulded edges of the case and the tube and the illusion is extended to the hinged cistern cover which encloses the portable screw. The register plates and vernier are of ivory with the weather indications limited to Fair, Change and Rain. This particular maker, Gardners of Glasgow, was known to use the word Serene rather than Fair on occasions, whilst another maker, A. Bellamy of Poultry, London, preferred the word Doubtful to Change on some of his barometers. The name of Gardner was well known in Glasgow as general instrument makers between 1765 and 1860 and this barometer can be dated 1822.

The Negretti & Zambra partnership was formed in 1850 by Enrico (Henry) Negretti and Joseph Zambra as makers of scientific instruments. It expanded rapidly and became a public company in 1948 under the name of Negretti & Zambra Limited and trades successfully today, specialising in instrumentation and control systems, from its registered office at Aylesbury, Buckinghamshire.

In the 1850s Negretti & Zambra were offering a wide choice of stick or pediment barometers, as they were then called, for domestic use. The cases were made of either mahogany, rosewood, ebony, oak or walnut and could be obtained in either plain designs or handsomely and elaborately carved and embellished, in a variety of designs suitable for private homes, large halls or public buildings. The register plates and thermometer scales could be of ivory, porcelain or silvered brass. Two verniers and two weather indications could also be fitted, one on each side of the mercury tube, so that one could register the last reading and so show at a glance the extent of rise or fall in the interval. The cheap instruments had open faces and plain frames with a sliding vernier instead of a rack-and-pinion mechanism, whilst the more expensive types had the benefit of plate glass to protect the register plates and thermometer. In addition, barometers could be made to specific requirements.

The types of barometers advertised by Negretti & Zambra in the 1850s were made until late in the nineteenth century so that it is difficult to date individual

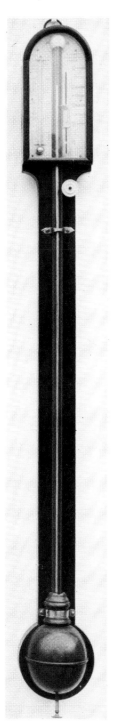

instruments with any accuracy. In fact, the type of barometer shown in *Fig.* 32, (p.30), known as a portable model barometer, was made until the beginning of the twentieth century.

A further difficulty in dating barometers becomes apparent around this time, as it was common practice for makers to engrave the retailer's name and address on the register plates rather than their own. This was at the request of the retailer who considered that his own standing and reputation would be enhanced if the impression was given that he was the maker. However, it is sometimes possible to establish the name of the maker by looking at the back of the case to see if there are any operating instructions. Some considerate makers made a point of pasting instructions for setting up the barometer on the back of the frame and added their name and address.

The barometer in *Fig.* 28 was made by Negretti & Zambra but the retailer's name, 'W. Lund, 23 & 24 Fleet Str^t. London', is engraved on the register plates. The following printed 'Instructions for the Barometer' by Negretti & Zambra are pasted on the back of the case:

Suspend the Barometer on a hook or stout nail preferably with a round head. Insert the key (found just below the scales) to the square brass pin at the lower end of the instrument, turn gently towards the left hand till the screw stops. Then remove the key and return it for use near the scales as it was before. The cistern bottom being thus let down, the mercury will quickly sink to its proper level.

In removing the Barometer it is necessary to slope it gradually till the mercury has risen to the top of the tube, and then with the instrument reversed, to screw up the cistern by means of the key, use gently till it

Fig. 28. Rosewood cistern barometer by Negretti & Zambra, c. 1850.

Fig. 29. Rosewood cistern barometer by W. & T. C. Heath, Devonport, c. 1850.

stops. It will then be portable with the lower end uppermost or lying flat, but it must not be jarred or receive a concussion.

The frame is veneered with rosewood and has the then popular round-top hood, which supports the glass protecting the ivory register plates and mercury thermometer. The thermometer carries both the Fahrenheit and Reaumur scale and the vernier is adjusted by the key below the hood. The hemispherical cistern cover is not original as it should have a flat turned cover similar to the one shown in *Fig.* 29. The square brass pin, referred to in the instructions, has also been replaced by a hand-adjustable screw making the use of the key unnecessary.

Rosewood appears to have been the most popular wood for making barometers for a limited time around the middle of the nineteenth century and *Fig.* 29 shows another rosewood instrument which is typical of this period. It is very similar to the one illustrated in *Fig.* 28, the main difference being that the case is panelled and so encloses the tube. This barometer is in its original condition with the vernier key used to adjust the squared cistern screw. The weather indications and thermometer scales are identical and the only difference within the hood is that the ivory register plates are set aslant. This arrangement was adopted when making the narrow marine barometer at the beginning of the century and it was used in order to gain width across the plates without widening the hood. From about 1840 the practice became common in domestic barometers, where the plates were protected by glass.

The name engraved on the plates is 'W. & T. C. Heath, Devonport', and there is recorded a William and Thomas Cornish Heath who traded as barometer makers and opticians at 46 Fore Street, Devonport, between 1850 and 1852.

Fig. 30. Rosewood cistern barometer by Webb, Taunton, c. 1860.

Fig. 31. Oak cistern barometer by Elliot Bros., London, c. 1

An example of a barometer with two verniers and duplicate weather indications is shown in *Fig.* 30. The panelled case is again veneered with rosewood and, as there is no room on the register plates for a thermometer, it is housed in its own glazed case on the main trunk. A mercury thermometer is used with Fahrenheit and Reaumur scales on an ivory plate. The ivory register plates have identical weather indications on each side of the tube with the additional engraving of '10 a. m. Yesterday' on the left-hand plate and '10 a. m. To-day' on the right-hand plate. With the two verniers, controlled by the two keys below the hood, it was intended to read the barometer daily at 10 a. m. so that day-to-day comparisons could be made. The name on the register plates is 'Webb, Taunton', who has not been traced, which suggests that he was probably only a retailer. The barometer was made around 1860.

Around this time it appears that oak was becoming increasingly popular and solid oak cases were extensively used during the last quarter of the nineteenth century, with mahogany and rosewood being used to a decreasing extent. The solid oak frame barometer in *Fig.* 31 is particularly interesting because it is fitted with porcelain register plates which are seldom found on extant barometers. The brass reading indicator in the form of two joined rings is unusual, as also is the cistern cover, the shape being reminiscent of contemporary cups and tankards.

The barometer can be dated about 1860 and was made by Elliott Bros. of 449 Strand, London. The brothers were Charles and Frederick, the sons of William Elliott who, as a young man in 1795, was apprenticed to one William Backwell, a London maker of compasses and drawing instruments. The indenture is of interest as it throws light on the considerable control the master exercised over his apprentice at that time. The following is an extract:

He shall not . . . contract matrimony within the said term. He shall not play at cards, dice tables or any other unlawful games . . . He shall not haunt taverns or playhouses nor absent himself from his master's service day or night unlawfully but in all things as a faithful apprentice he shall behave himself towards his said master and all during the said term . . .

Owing to the death of his master, William Elliott was unable to complete his 7 years' apprenticeship and in 1800 he started in business on his own making drawing instruments. He soon diversified and in 1816, it is recorded, he made a large magic lantern for Her Grace, the Duchess of Wellington, for which he charged 34/-. The sons were taken into partnership in 1830 and the business was well established at 449, Strand before 1860. In 1857 the partnership took over the business of Watkins & Hill, who were instrument makers and who made the unusual wheel barometer shown in *Fig.* 77 (p.76). Elliott Bros. now forms part of the G. E. C.-Elliott Automation Group.

The most popular type of stick barometer ever made must have been the model barometer illustrated in *Fig.* 32. It is made of solid oak with open register plates, but the bulb of the Fahrenheit mercury thermometer is protected by a wide brass loop. The register plates are of ivory with the standard weather indications. The leather-based cistern is fitted with a screw to make it portable. The name engraved is 'Hanny, Shrewsbury'.

This type of barometer must have been sold for a period of 50 years extending into the first decade of the twentieth century. In 1875 the sale price was 13/-6d.

with 3/- extra for enamel plates. In 1885 the price — with ivory plates — had risen to one guinea.

During the last quarter of the nineteenth century a very large selection of stick or pediment barometers were made. A catalogue issued by James J. Hicks of 8 Hatton Gardens, London, in 1875 gave the prices of 44 different pediment barometers of which 21 were illustrated. They were mainly large, carved, solid oak instruments with pediments described variously as shield top, shield and point, pointed top, ecclesiastical, round top, castellated top, square top and dome top. The cistern covers were round, square or rectangular and heavily carved. Thermometers were invariably mounted on the trunk and the glazed hood contained enamel or ivory register plates set aslant. Two verniers were fitted and Fitzroy words (q.v.) were used for the weather indications.

These large and ornate barometers were not really intended for domestic use, but they were popular in institutions, church halls and public buildings. Descriptions of two of the barometers in the catalogue will give a better idea of their appearance. The Exchange or Reading Room Barometer was described thus:

'In massive oak frame elaborately carved, with pillar at side, in Ionic design, very bold tube and broad enamelled glass scales. This barometer has an imposing appearance, and is well adapted for Public Institutions.'

The Torricelli–Debrel Barometer (Registered) was described thus:

'The frame of this instrument is elaborately carved in the Italian Renaissance style, and is surmounted by a carved head of Torricelli, under which are the words in antique letter

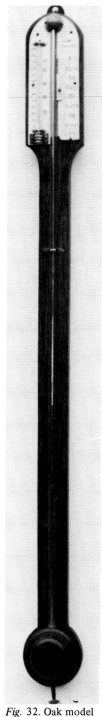

Fig. 32. Oak model barometer by Hanny, Shrewsbury, c. 1875.

Fig. 33. Oak pediment barometer by J. H. Steward, London, c. 1875.

30

"Torricelli invt. 1643". A highly sensitive spiral thermometer is attached, with Fahrenheit and Celsius scales, and surmounted by a carved head of Drebel, the inventor of the thermometer, with words also in antique letter "Drebel invt. 1620" under the head. In addition to being a most handsome piece of furniture for the hall or library, the instrument thus assumes an educational character.'

The square moulded pediment barometer in *Fig.* 33 was made c. 1875 and gives an idea of the construction of the instruments sold by James J. Hicks, but it is, by comparison, very small and without any carving or decoration. The frame is of solid oak with a square moulded top and flat turned cistern cover. The cistern tube is portable and the mercury thermometer has both Fahrenheit and Reaumur scales. The thermometer and register plates are protected by glass and there are two verniers. Ivory is used for both sets of scales and the maker's name, J. H. Steward, 54 Cornhill, London, is engraved on the left-hand register plate. On the right-hand plate is engraved 'Add one tenth for each ninety feet above sea level'. This relates to a correction in the reading which is necessary if the barometer is used other than at sea level.

During the second half of the nineteenth century the aneroid barometer was becoming increasingly popular at the expense of the mercury instrument, but stick or pediment barometers were still made in small numbers until about 1905 when it was eventually displaced by the less expensive, more compact and thoroughly portable aneroid barometer. However, in 1919 reproductions began to appear and continue to be made to this day. These are mainly copies of the portable model barometer in *Fig.* 32 and the broken-pediment barometer in *Fig.* 17.

3 Angle Tube Barometers

Shortly after it was realised that the extremes of atmospheric pressure only varied the height of a column of mercury by a maximum of 3 inches, many scientists considered ways and means of enlarging the reading by extending the scale. Various instruments were designed with this objective in mind, but it was Sir Samuel Morland who, in 1670, thought of a simple modification to the straight tube which achieved this result.

He bent a tube sharply to almost a right-angle just below the lowest point to which the mercury could fall and extended the arm for about 36 inches. The arm rose about 3 inches along its length so that for every inch the mercury rose it had to travel 12 inches along the arm, resulting in a scale magnification of twelve to one. The tube was bent between 27 and 28 inches above the level of the mercury in the cistern, and the scale extended from 28 to 31 inches along the angled tube. This was the basis of the angle tube barometer.

Samuel Morland was the son of Thomas Morland, rector of Sullamstead Bannister, Berkshire. He became a mathematician and also invented the balance barometer, of which only a very few were made as they had a number of disadvantages. His most important work was in the field of hydrostatics, and he invented an apparatus using an airtight cistern from which air was expelled by a charge of gunpowder, the water below rising to fill the vacuum produced. There was great interest in the mid-seventeenth century in mechanical methods of raising water and Morland was the leader in this field. King Charles II, who knighted him, named him 'Master of Mechanics' in 1681. He married five times, but was survived by only one son, called Samuel.

The angle barometer was never regarded as a scientific instrument as its accuracy was impaired by the shape of the mercury meniscus, which varied between rising and falling conditions so offsetting the effect of the magnified scale; the reading was also affected by friction between the mercury and the tube. However, as a domestic barometer it achieved some popularity and was produced, although not continuously, until 1860. Because of their appearance they were variously called sign post, yard arm, inclined or diagonal barometers.

This type of barometer was not, at first, very popular because of its shape, and John Smith, when writing about the barascope or quicksilver weather-glass in 1688, noted that 'These do manifest the least motions of the mercury more visibly than that with the straight tube', and also that 'This form was but seldom used being such as will not admit of any regular figure'.

One of the earliest angle barometer makers was Daniel Quare, and a particularly fine example by him can be seen at Hampton Court. The frame is of turned walnut similar in appearance to the Quare barometer in *Fig. 4*, and the silvered brass register plates are 20 inches in length and cover a 2 inch rise in the mercury from 28·5 inches to 30·5 inches, a magnification of ten. The barometer was made about the beginning of the eighteenth century.

Another early maker was John Patrick, an instrument maker, who advertised diagonal barometers during the first decade of the eighteenth century. He overcame the main criticism that the barometer lacked balance by mounting it on a square or rectangular frame and incorporated a large looking-glass in the central section. To balance the vertical section of the mercury tube at one side of the frame he added a large thermometer at the other side and used identical covers for the cistern and the thermometer bulb. He advertised the instrument as follows:

> An excellent diagonal barometer with a looking-glass commodiously placed on the same frame, between the barometer and the thermometer, whereby gentlemen and ladies at the same time they dress may accommodate their habit to the weather – an invention not only curious but also profitable and pleasant.

Patrick sold this type of barometer for 15 guineas in 1710, the lay-out being similar to the barometer shown in *Fig. 35*.

Comparatively few angle barometers were made during the eighteenth century as the stick barometer was by far the most popular. However, a variety was made by a limited number of makers, the main difference between them being the length of the arm. It was, of course, easy to increase the length of the scale by reducing the angle of the tube and some barometers were made with the horizontal section of the tube twice as long as the vertical.

Such barometers were unsightly and unwieldy, and a way of reducing the horizontal length without reducing the scale was devised. This was to use two or three separate tubes, set side by side, with each one angled at a slightly different height so that the two or three horizontal tubes would cover the full scale. For example, if there were three tubes and the scale was to extend from 28 inches to 31 inches, the first tube would be angled at 28 inches, the second at 29 inches and the third at 30 inches. Each horizontal section would rise 1 inch along its length so that when the reading was 29½ inches, the lower horizontal tube would be full with the middle tube half full and the upper tube empty.

The idea of using two or three tubes is attributed to Charles Orme (1688–1747) of Ashby-de-la-Zouch, Leicestershire, and a double-tube angle barometer made by him is shown in *Fig. 34*. The case is 6½ inches wide and is veneered with walnut, whilst decoration takes the form of brass inlays incorporating a fleur-de-lis motif. The silvered brass register plates are protected by glass and there are standard weather indications of Great Drought, Set Fair, Fair and Changeable against the upper tube and Changeable, Rain, Much Rain and Stormy against the lower tube. The scale covers a range of 3 inches, from 28 to 31, and is graduated in hundredths of an inch. There is a ring recording device fitted to each tube and these are adjusted by wormed rods controlled by the two brass knobs at the extreme right-hand side of the case.

The register plate is engraved 'Made by Charles Orme of Ashby-de-la-Zouch 1742'. He was a distinguished barometer maker and made angle barometers with one, two or three tubes, using boxwood cisterns. Other important contemporary makers were Edward Scarlett (1688–1743) and Jonathan Sisson (1690–1747).

The early angle barometers were veneered in walnut but mahogany was preferred from around the middle of the eighteenth century. A few were lacquered with japan to make them black and glossy and some were decorated with marquetry: a later decoration was the use of inlays, including the shell motif, on cistern covers, which became so popular on the wheel type of barometer.

Fig. 34. Double-tube angle barometer by C. Orme, dated 1742. (Reproduced by kind permission of the Curator of the City of Gloucester Museum.)

Fig. 35. Angle tube barometer with mirror, c. 1760. (Reproduced by kind permission of Sotheby's, London.)

34

Because of its unattractive shape and the difficulty in decorating it, the angle barometer never achieved the popularity of the stick and wheel varieties. Because of the limited demand there were comparatively few makers and the barometers they produced were generally of their own distinctive design. A second attempt was made, however, around 1750, to improve the shape by reintroducing a wall mirror. An example is shown in *Fig. 35*. The case is veneered with mahogany and the broken architectural pediment is centred with a brass finial in the shape of an urn. The barometer and Fahrenheit thermometer both have silvered brass plates and both are fitted with a sliding indicating pointer. Spirally turned cistern covers protect both instruments and a hygrometer is fitted centrally below the register plates. A spirit level is incorporated in the shaped apron and the overall height is 3 feet 4 inches. The barometer does not bear the maker's name, but it can be dated mid-eighteenth century.

An important maker of angle barometers in the third quarter of the eighteenth century was John Whitehurst (1723–88) who made the instrument in *Fig*. 36 about 1770. The oak case is veneered with mahogany and the silvered brass register plate is protected by glass which is fixed flush to the plate. The weather indications are standard, but the scale is unusual being from zero to 60, with Changeable or 29·5 inches being equivalent to 30; its length is a little under 21 inches, which gives a magnification of seven. The tube and solid-base boxwood cistern appear to be as originally fitted.

John Whitehurst is recorded as having started in business as a clockmaker in Derby in 1736; he became well known as a maker of turret, long-case and other clocks and was elected a Fellow of the Royal Society in 1779. In 1775, he moved to London to become 'Stamper of Money Weights' at the Mint, but still continued to make clocks. The business in Derby was subsequently carried on by his nephew, John Whitehurst, who continued to make similar angle barometers and also wheel barometers, one of which is illustrated in *Fig.* 49 (p.51). Both makers engraved their barometers 'Whitehurst, Derby' so that it is difficult to decide with certainty who made a particular barometer, although the words engraved on the register plates of instruments that can be attributed to the nephew bear far more ornamentation by way of flowing curves and flourishes.

Bapt. Roncheti, who has already been referred to as a prolific maker of stick, wheel and multiple-tube barometers, also made angle barometers, the one illustrated in *Fig*. 37 being by him. It was made very early in the nineteenth century and is veneered with mahogany. The silvered registered plates are 18 inches long and the scale is divided into tenths of an inch. A bulb cistern tube is used and the sliding ring recording indicator can be adjusted by the knob below the plates, which are engraved 'Bapt. Roncheti & Co'.

Other important makers of angle barometers during the second half of the eighteenth century were Francis Watkins (1723–84) and a partnership of Watkins & Smith formed by Francis Watkins and his apprentice Addison Smith.

Francis Watkins must have seen and admired the angle barometers made by John Patrick at the beginning of the century. He produced barometers very similar in design and lay-out, but instead of a large looking-glass he included a perpetual calendar called a 'Perpetual Regulation of Time'. (These were mentioned when describing the cistern barometer by Watkins shown in *Fig*. 14.)

No doubt Francis Watkins and Addison Smith were making a further attempt to popularise the angle barometer by giving it a balanced appearance; they made some

Fig. 36. Mahogany angle barometer by Whitehurst, Derby, c. 1770.

Fig. 37. Mahogany angle barometer by Bapt. Roncheti & Co., c. 1805. (Reproduced by kind permission of the Curator of the City of Gloucester Museum.)

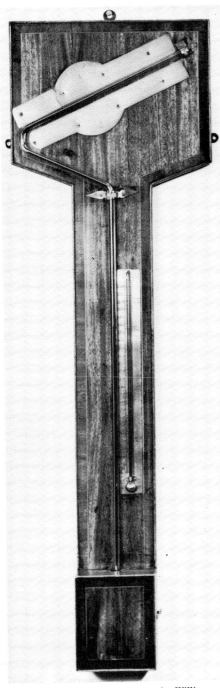

Fig. 38. Double-angle barometer by William Robb, c. 1800.

with broken and some with unbroken pediments, whilst an oat beard hygrometer was often fitted centrally above the calendar but below the register plates.

William Robb of Montrose in Scotland made an unusual design of angle barometer in the hope that it would become a more popular item of furniture – he produced double-angle barometers. One such barometer engraved with his name on the register plates is shown in *Fig.* 38. The case is veneered and cross-banded in mahogany with a fruitwood stringing, and this is repeated on the rectangular box cistern cover. The cover is not hinged and is kept in position by engaging two wooden pins protruding from the case and brass catches each side of the cover which fix to loops on the frame.

The double angle allows the tube to be housed on a symmetrical base with the 10 inch long silvered brass register plates extending to the full width of the frame. The scale is from 28 to 31 inches and covers 6½ inches with graduations of one-twentieth of an inch. A bulb cistern tube is used with a mercury thermometer and Fahrenheit scale. A small hole in the top right-hand corner of the register plates suggests that a manually operated reading indicator was originally fitted, which could be moved along a rod attached to the frame through the hole in the plates.

William Robb is recorded as being a long-case clockmaker in Montrose in 1776, and it appears that he remained in business there until early in the nineteenth century.

A similar double-angle barometer by Balthazar Knie can be seen in the City of Gloucester Museum. He was an immigrant German glassblower who settled in Edinburgh in 1774 and died in 1817. This design of barometer appears to have originated in Germany and Knie could well have remembered it and made copies. However, the design adopted by Robb more closely resembles the German

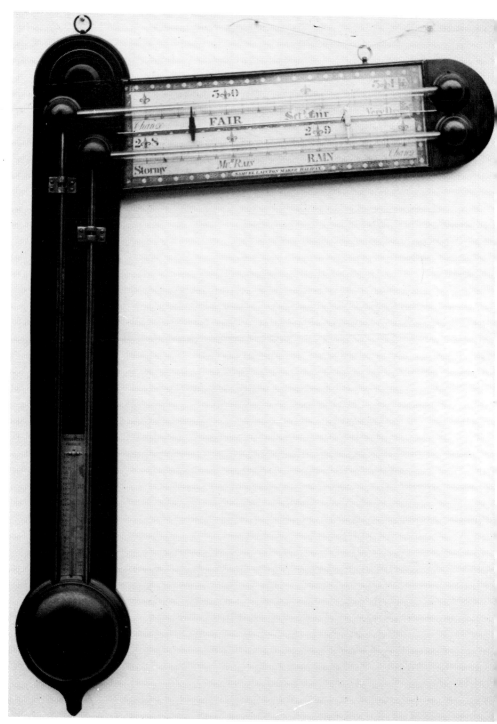

Fig. 39. Double-tube angle barometer by Samuel Lainton, c. 1850.

examples still extant, so it is difficult to decide which maker was the first to produce them around 1800. Knie and Robb appear to have been the only two makers to produce this type of barometer in the United Kingdom.

Apart from the angle barometers already described made by Roncheti, Knie and Robb, very few were produced in the nineteenth century by other makers, except Samuel Lainton and Charles Howarth, who both had addresses in Halifax, Yorkshire, and sold almost identical angle barometers around 1850.

An example by Lainton is shown in *Fig*. 39. The case is veneered in mahogany, whilst the shallow turned bulb cistern cover is of solid mahogany, as are the four circular caps which support the tubes. The printed paper register plates are protected by glass and the 3 inch actual scale is magnified ten times. Standard weather indications are used with Change repeated at the lower end of the upper tube and at the upper end of the lower tube. The scale is calibrated to one-hundredths of an inch and there are several masonic signs at the right-hand end of the upper scale. 'Samuel Lainton Maker Halifax' is printed along the bottom of the lower scale. A brass recording pointer for each scale can be manually operated along the brass rod between the two tubes. Mercury is used in the Fahrenheit thermometer which is engraved 'Warranted Correct' and the thermometer bulb is contained within the cistern cover.

An identical double-tube barometer by Lainton can be seen in the Whipple Museum, Cambridge, and a very similar instrument by Howarth is on view in the Museum of the History of Science, Oxford University.

Lainton and Howarth also made single-tube angle barometers; these have narrower frames and extended arms using similar paper register plates, but in this case they are positioned side by side rather than one above the other. These would appear to be the last type of angle barometers made as a commercial proposition.

4 Marine and Sea Coast Barometers

There is some doubt as to when the first barometer was used at sea, but there is evidence that in 1667 the scientist Robert Hooke appreciated the advantage of mariners being able to measure the air pressure whilst at sea.

The main problem was to prevent the oscillation of the mercury in the tube caused by the motions of the ship, and Hooke conducted a number of experiments in an endeavour to overcome this. He presented a paper to the Royal Society in which he suggested two successful methods. The first consisted of an air thermometer, with mercury as an indicating liquid, and a spirit thermometer to record the temperature. The variations in air pressure were recorded by the rise or fall of the mercury in the air thermometer with adjustments being made for temperature after reference to the spirit thermometer. This instrument was taken on a voyage of exploration in the Atlantic in 1698 by Edmond Halley, who reported that it never failed to give early notice of all the bad weather. Such an instrument was advertised by John Patrick in 1710 as 'A ship's barometer a foot long'. It was in use for many years and should, perhaps, have been more correctly described as a thermobarometer. This instrument was eventually replaced by the sympiesometer which was patented in 1818 by Alexander Adie of Edinburgh, who entitled the patent 'An improvement on the air barometer'. The sympiesometer is described later in Chapter 6.

The second method was to constrict the tube to a fine bore at the lower end, just above the cistern, and this had the effect of containing the oscillations to an acceptable level.

Nothing further appears to have happened to this invention until 1773 – more than a hundred years later – when an improved form of constricted-tube barometer was taken on a scientific voyage towards the North Pole undertaken by His Majesty's Command. The officer in charge, Captain C. J. Phipps, Second Baron Mulgrave, published an account of the voyage and described the instruments aboard, which included a marine barometer made by a Mr Edward Nairne. The bore of the upper part of the glass tube was about three-tenths of an inch in diameter and 4 inches long. To this was joined a glass tube with a bore about one-twentieth of an inch in diameter. The two glass tubes were joined together to form the barometer tube. The instrument was attached to a gimbal and kept in a perpendicular position by a weight fastened to the cistern cover. This type of construction proved to be successful at sea and was used for upwards of a hundred years.

Edward Nairne (1726–1806) has already been mentioned as the partner of Thomas Blunt. He was an optical, mathematical and philosophical instrument maker and published literature on astronomical and navigational instruments. He made diagonal, portable and marine barometers at his workshop at 20 Cornhill, London.

It will be appreciated that the demand for marine barometers was limited and they were not made in any relatively large quantity until the beginning of the nineteenth century.

Fig. 40 illustrates an early marine barometer made by Jones of 338 Strand, London, c. 1815. The top eight inches of the tube has a bore of approximately three-tenths of an inch whilst the remainder of the tube has a bore with a diameter little more than that of a pin. The tube is cemented to the cistern, which is made of boxwood and has a leather base for the purpose of making the barometer portable by screwing up the mercury to the top of the tube. The tube is enclosed in a solid mahogany frame which has a hinged door to be opened when a reading is taken. The silvered brass register plates are set aslant, to give an increased width, and a manual vernier is fitted. The plates are calibrated from 27 to 31 inches and the following standard weather indications are used: Very Dry, Set Fair, Fair, Change, Rain, Much Rain and Stormy.

A Fahrenheit mercury thermometer with a silvered brass scale is mounted on the inside of the door and is fully protected when the door is closed. The barometer can be hung on a wall or mounted on a gimbal, for which there is a hole on each side of the case. The boxwood cistern is ebonised on the outside and can be unscrewed from the case. Its weight, together with the weight of the mercury it contains, is sufficient to ensure that the barometer moves on the bearings and always remains in an upright position.

The maker's name is engraved on a brass plate above the door and as there is an identical marine barometer on show in the Science Museum, London, made by Thomas Jones of 62 Charing Cross, London, it is reasonable to assume that he made both barometers. Jones traded from various addresses in London between 1806 and 1850 and became an authority on astronomical and meteorological instruments. He also made mountain and domestic siphon-tube barometers.

This type of marine barometer was in general use until 1853, when an international conference was called in Brussels for the purpose of devising a systematic plan for promoting meteorological observations at sea. Various recommendations were made by the Brussels Conference and these were adopted by the British Government, who encouraged the Kew Committee of the British Association to develop a marine barometer, incorporating the recommendations, at the Kew Observatory.

By 1855 a Kew marine barometer had emerged. It was in shape similar to the one already described, except that the glass tube was protected by a brass tubular frame into which screwed an iron cistern. A thermometer was fixed to the frame a few inches above the cistern with its bulb enclosed in the frame so that its heat would be the same as the mercury in the tube. A brass ring, movable in a collar fixed on the frame above the centre of gravity of the barometer, was attached to a gimbal and supported by a brass arm. The tube was still

Fig. 40. Mahogany marine barometer by Jones, 338 Strand, London, c. 1815.

41

considerably restricted for the greater part of its length, in order to reduce oscillations or pumping of the mercury caused by the ship's motion. A Bunten air trap was also incorporated below the narrow part of the tube; this consisted of an elongated funnel with the point downwards set in the centre of the tube, rather like a pipette, which prevented any air working its way up between the glass and the mercury to reach the vacuum. Glass protected the silvered brass register plates and a vernier allowed readings to five-hundredths of an inch. No words were used on the register plates as these were deemed to be misleading.

This type of barometer continued to be made with little variation until the beginning of the twentieth century, when it was finally replaced by the aneroid barometer. The Board of Trade standard barometer (or Kew marine barometer) shown in *Fig.* 42 was made towards the end of the century and is very similar, except that it lacks a thermometer.

It was evident that this type of barometer was more reliable in its performance than those with wooden frames. The metal frame allowed the tube to be held more rigidly and the graduations could be more accurately made, with only temperature having an effect on the readings. The Admiralty favoured the metal-cased barometer, but in spite of this the wooden case was preferred by some, mainly for its handsome appearance.

Fig. 41 shows a pleasing marine barometer which was made about 1870. The bow-fronted case is of solid mahogany with a square moulded pediment and attractive carving above the brass cistern cover. The cistern tube is constricted and there is a portable screw within the cistern cover. The ivory register plates are set aslant and are protected by bow glass. They have duplicate weather indications and two verniers, so that comparisons can be made on a day-to-day basis at 10 a. m. The thermometer has its own glazed case fixed to the trunk and the ivory scales have Fahrenheit and Raeumur calibrations with the usual words: Fever Heat, Blood Heat, Summer Heat, Temperate and Freezing.

The maker's or retailer's name engraved on the register plates is 'C. G. Brander & Son, 82, Minories, London'.

The cases for this type of barometer varied from maker to maker with the pediments being either round top, carved or square moulded. The carving above the cistern also varied in form, with some being just plain bow-fronted. A sympieso-meter — which is explained later — was often fitted in place of a thermometer if it was required to make accurate and comparative observations. In this case the tube of the sympiesometer had to be contracted to prevent oscillation. Being extremely sensitive and of convenient size, the sympiesometer was used instead of a barometer for marine

Fig. 41. Mahogany marine barometer by C. G. Brander & Son, London, c. 1870.

observations for a period, but owing to its tendency to be put out of adjustment in transit, it was relegated to an instrument of comparison.

The name of Admiral Fitzroy (1805–65) is associated with marine barometers. He was the son of Lord Charles Fitzroy and joined the Royal Navy in 1819. He was Member of Parliament for Durham in 1841 and appointed Governor of New Zealand in 1843. On retirement from active service in 1850 he continued to rise in rank by reason of seniority and became a Vice-Admiral in 1863. In retirement he turned his attentions to the science of meteorology and was appointed Meteorological Officer to the Board of Trade in 1854. He considered that the Kew marine barometer was not practical for general use because it was too delicate in construction, difficult to read and was likely to be broken by the firing of a ship's guns. He therefore set about designing a barometer which would overcome these faults and issued the following description:

This marine barometer, for Her Majesty's service, is adapted to general purposes. It differs from barometers hitherto made in points of detail, rather than principle:
1. The glass tube is packed with vulcanised india rubber, which checks vibration from concussion; but does not hold it rigidly, or prevent expansion.
2. It does not oscillate (or pump), though extremely sensitive.
3. The scale is porcelain, very legible, and not liable to change.
4. There is no iron anywhere (to rust).
5. Every part can be unscrewed, examined, or cleaned, by any careful person.
6. There is a spare tube, fixed in a cistern, filled with boiled mercury, and marked for adjustment in this, or any similar instrument.

The barometer is graduated in hundredths, and will be found accurate to that degree, namely the second decimal of an inch. It is packed with vulcanised caoutchouc, in order that (by this, and by a peculiar strength of glass tube) guns may be fired near the instrument without causing injury to it by ordinary concussion. It is hoped that all such instruments, for the public service at sea, will be quite similar, so that any spare tube will fit any barometer.

Messrs Negretti & Zambra made these barometers for the Royal Navy and their appearance is identical to the one shown in *Fig.* 42 except that they have a thermometer on the brass trunk of the case and Admiral Fitzroy's words on the scale. The graduation of inches and decimals are engraved on the right-hand side of the porcelain register plate, with a vernier, and on the left-hand side plate is engraved, as legibly as they are expressed succinctly, the following words of interpretation of the barometer movements:

RISE	FALL
for	for
COLD	WARM
DRY	WET
or	or
LESS	MORE
WIND	WIND

The tube had a boxwood cistern, which was plugged with very porous cane at the top, to allow an immediate reaction of the mercury to any change in atmospheric pressure. The barometer could be hung from the brass ring or attached to a gimbal.

This barometer was called the Fitzroy marine or gun marine barometer and was sold by a number of makers from 1860. Messrs Negretti & Zambra appear to have been involved in its development, as in their *Treatise on Meteorological Instruments* dated 1864 there is a very interesting description of trials of the Fitzroy marine barometer under fire of guns, some of which Mr Negretti attended. The purpose of the trials was to ascertain whether the vulcanised india rubber packing round the glass tube of the new marine barometer did check the vibration caused by firing. In a series of experiments a new Fitzroy barometer was tested side by side with a Kew type barometer on HMS *Excellent*. They were hung over the gun, under the gun, by the side of the gun and both inside and outside a bulkhead. The result was that the Kew type barometer was broken and rendered useless, whilst the Fitzroy barometer was not damaged. Five Fitzroy barometers were then subjected to the concussion produced by firing a 68-pounder gun with shot, and 16lb charge of powder. They were suspended under the gun, then over the gun and finally by a gimbal to a bulkhead at a distance of only 3 feet 6 inches from the axis of the gun. The official report stated that all these barometers, however suspended, would stand, without the slightest injury, the most severe concussion that they would ever be likely to experience in any sea-going man-of-war.

These barometers, like the Kew marine, continued to be made until they were eventually replaced completely by the aneroid barometer early in the twentieth century.

The Board of Trade standard, or Kew marine barometer in *Fig.* 42 was made about 1900. It is mounted in a bronzed metal frame and has all the improvements to prevent the mercury pumping in bad weather, as recommended by the Brussels Conference for Marine Meteorological Observations in 1853. The appearance of this kind of barometer had not changed for 50 years, except that the words on the register plates were replaced by a millimetre scale during the last quarter of the nineteenth century.

Whilst keen to perfect the marine barometer, Admiral Fitzroy was also concerned that fishermen and others, whose lives were endangered by sudden changes in the weather, should have the benefit of being able to consult a barometer. His persistence persuaded the Board of Trade, in the early 1860s, to provide, at public expense, a fishery or sea coast barometer in many towns and villages, fixed in a prominent position, so that anyone who wished to consult it could do so.

Following this example, the Royal National Life Boat Institution supplied each of its stations with a similar barometer, whilst the Duke of Northumberland and the British Meteorological Society erected several on the coast of Northumberland.

Such a barometer is shown in *Fig.* 43. The frame is of solid oak with a rounded top and flat square cistern cover. The cistern tube is portable and the mercury thermometer has both Fahrenheit and Centigrade scales. The thermometer and register plates are protected by glass and there are two verniers. Porcelain is used for both sets of scales and the maker's name, 'Ross, London', is engraved above the register plates. On the right-hand plate is engraved 'Add one tenth for each ninety feet above sea level'. The register plates are shown in detail

in *Fig.* 44.

The weather indications on the register plates are given below and are known as Admiral Fitzroy's scale words:

RISE	FALL
for	for
N.ELY.	S.WLY.
NW. N. E.	SE. S. W.

DRY	WET
or	or
LESS	MORE
WIND	WIND

EXCEPT	EXCEPT
WET	WET
FROM N. ED	FROM N. ED

Admiral Fitzroy realised that the standard weather indications previously used were not accurate statements of the weather conditions when taken from the level of the mercury at any particular time. He was more concerned with whether the mercury was rising or falling, the force and direction of the wind and the humidity of the atmosphere. His words illustrate that the warm winds of Europe are those which bring the greatest quantity of rain, as they blow from the ocean and come heavily laden with moisture. The cold winds blow more from the land and contain less moisture.

These barometers proved to be very successful, as is shown by an extract from Admiral Fitzroy's report of the Meteorological Office to the Board of Trade in 1864:

In my last report I stated how highly the Board of Trade 'Fishery Barometers have been valued on the coasts. They are now eighty in all, specially lent, under due control and care. Two only of this number have become slightly defective, and have been exchanged. Not one has

Fig. 42. Board of Trade standard or Kew marine barometer, c. 1900.

Fig. 43. Oak sea coast barometer by Ross, London, c. 1865.

Fig. 44. Detail of *Fig.* 43.

been injured in carriage, singular to say, between Cornwall and the Shetland Isles, Ireland and Yorkshire. It may be more readily estimated mentally than accurately proved, to what extent these simple instruments (all reliably made and tested) have already been the means of saving life and property. Explanatory manuals and blank forms for diagrams have been extensively circulated among the coasters and fishermen, who are all, now, much influenced by, and very thankful for, the benefits of this act of their Government. Many are the local instances of similar beneficence by individuals — especially the Duke of Northumberland, who has placed no less than fourteen barometers.

In 1854 Admiral Fitzroy was appointed Chief of the Meteorological Department of the Board of Trade and was author of official reports to the Board from 1857 to 1865. He was associated with Charles Darwin (1809–82) with surveys aboard HMS *Beagle*, and in 1863 published his *Weather Book*, which summarised his considerable work on meteorology. He also set up a series of weather stations which would telegraph weather data to the Meteorological Office in London. Using this information he produced some of the first weather charts and began issuing weather forecasts. By the end of 1860 *The Times* was printing daily weather forecasts and Fitzroy was gaining recognition as the man who could predict coming weather conditions.

Unfortunately Fitzroy had a number of opponents, and some of his critics wanted the general theories of the science of Meteorology established before weather predictions were made public. In the midst of this controversy his mind became unbalanced and, sadly, he took his own life in 1865 when he was aged 60.

5 Wheel Barometers

The wheel barometer evolved from a desire to extend the scale of the barometer so that a more accurate reading could be taken. Its invention is attributed to Robert Hooke, who was the son of a clergyman, born in 1635 on the Isle of Wight. He became a brilliant engineer and invented the air pump in its enduring form. It is said that he added something to every important instrument developed in the seventeenth century and he has been called the founder of scientific meteorology.

In the early 1660s he was working as Robert Boyle's assistant, and it was in 1663 that he devised the wheel barometer as shown by a simple sketch in *Fig.* 45. His idea was to bend the open end of the tube into a U shape and use the mercury level in the short arm to record air pressure changes. A float rests on the mercury and is connected to a slightly lighter float by a thread which passes over a pulley. The arbor of the pulley wheel is connected to a pointer which circumambulates a dial. A movement of the mercury up or down in the tube will raise or lower the float which, in turn, will rotate the pulley. This will, of course, rotate the pointer and the movement of the mercury can be greatly amplified on the dial scale. This type of tube, known as the siphon tube, is used in reproduction wheel barometers to this day, and an example is shown in *Fig.* 46. As can be seen, there has been little variation in the design except that the diameter of the top section of the tube has been substantially reduced. Glass floats have replaced the metal ones with the balance float contained within an empty short glass tube so that it can rise and fall without restriction.

The siphon tube or wheel barometer was never developed as a scientific instrument and its sale was confined to the domestic market. Very few appear to have been made until the second half of the eighteenth century and it is thought that the first was made by the famous clockmaker Thomas Tompion (1638–1713) for Robert Hooke around 1675. Like his clocks, the barometers made by Tompion are of an exceptionally high quality; very few have survived, but two can be seen in Hampton Court.

George Graham (1673–1751), who succeeded Tompion on his death, made a small number of barometers of very high quality, but a more prolific maker was John Hallifax of Barnsley (1694–1750). He was the son of a vicar and started in business in 1711. He soon became a notable clock and barometer maker and a number of his barometers still survive. They are all of distinctive form and the design of the cases and dials were influenced by the shape and line of his long-case clocks.

An example is shown in *Fig.* 47, which can be dated c. 1730. The case is attractively veneered with a light brown walnut and the bezel containing the glazed dial is also of walnut. The chapter ring is of silvered brass and the brass centre of the dial is engraved 'John Hallifax, Barnsley. Invt. & Fect.' The weather indications are: Very Dry, Settled Fair, Fair or Frost, Changeable, Rain or Wind, Much Rain and Tempestuous. The full circle covers a 3 inch change in pressure from 28 inches to 31 inches and the dial is numbered one to thirty so that each

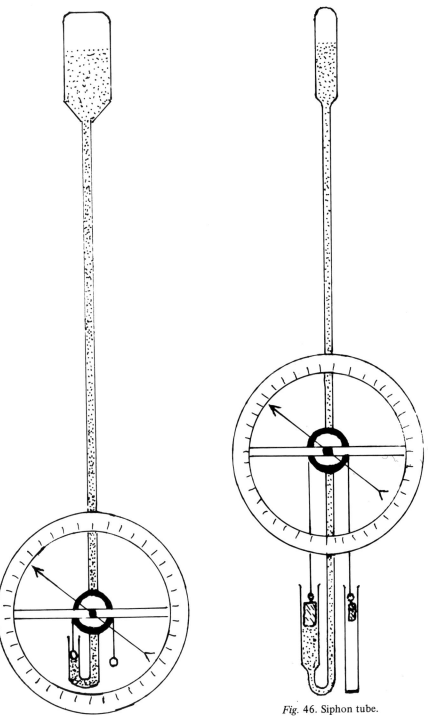

Fig. 46. Siphon tube.

Fig. 45. Sketch of Hooke's wheel barometer.

Fig. 47. Walnut wheel barometer by
John Hallifax, Barnsley, c. 1730.

division represents a movement of one-
tenth of an inch. This calibration is
repeated on the silvered brass recording
dial which has two steel hands, one to
record the previous reading and the other
to record the day of the month the reading was taken. The usual siphon tube is
used, but a cylinder is fitted in place of a
pulley which is rotated by a balance
system to which wire weights are
attached. The overall height is 45 inches
and the width of the case is 5 inches. Two
barometers by John Hallifax can be seen
in the Victoria and Albert Museum,
London; one is very similar to the one
described and the other, which has its
dial at the top of a heavily hooded case,
could easily be mistaken for a long-case
clock.

Hallifax was regarded as one of the
leading provincial clockmakers of his
day; this was acknowledged on his death
as his tomb stone was engraved 'Whose
abilities and virtue few in these times
have attained. His art and industry were
such as his ingenious inventions will be a
lasting monument of his merit − such as
recommended him to the favour and
esteem of all good men that knew him.'

He had seven children and one of
them, called Thomas, became Lord Mayor
of London in 1777.

Other well-known instrument makers
and clockmakers who made a very
limited number of wheel barometers,
probably to order, were George Adams
(1707−72) and his two sons George
Adams (1750−95) and Dudley Adams
(1760−1826) − all three traded at one
time or another in Fleet Street, London −
John Ellicott of London (1706−72), who
also incorporated wheel barometers in the
doors of some of his long-case clocks,
John Russell of Falkirk, Scotland (1745−
1817), John Whitehurst of Derby (1713−
88) and his nephew John Whitehurst
(1761−1834). All these makers produced
distinctive barometers of exceptional
quality to their own design which, in some

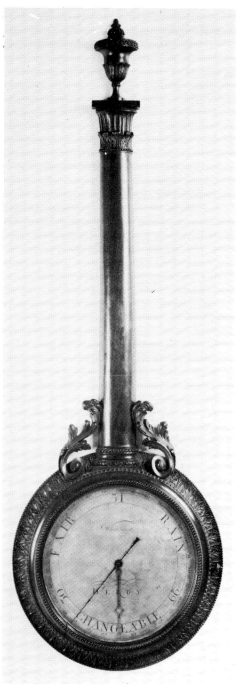

Fig. 49. Mahogany wheel barometer by John Whitehurst of Derby, c. 1800. (Reproduced by kind permission of Sotheby's, London.)

Fig. 48. Mahogany wheel barometer by John Russell of Falkirk, c. 1815. (Reproduced by kind permission of Christies, London.)

51

cases, was influenced in style by the clocks they made.

A Regency mahogany wheel barometer by John Russell of Falkirk is illustrated in *Fig.* 48. The overall height is 4 feet 6 inches and the case is mounted with gilt brass rope-twist mouldings and surmounted with Prince of Wales feathers. It has glass panels of black and gilt verre églomisé above and below the dial, the lower panel having a thistle design. The thermometer set in the upper panel is marked with the scale of the Royal Society as well as those of Reaumur and Fahrenheit. The whitened dial is engraved 'J. Russell, Falkirk, Invt. et Fecit. Watch Maker to his R. H. the Prince Regent', and contains two subsidiary micrometer dials; the upper dial is operated through cogs by the indicating mechanism and allows readings to one hundredth of an inch, whilst the lower dial is for recording purposes and, like the main set hand, is operated manually by the two visible wormed rods. The float of the barometer is loaded with mercury and has its own adjusting screw.

This fine instrument formed part of the Holyrood House collection and a similar barometer is on view in the Victoria and Albert Museum, London. Russell was a well-known maker of musical clocks and presented two barometers to King George III, one of which is similar to that illustrated and is at Buckingham Palace.

An important 10 inch wheel barometer made by John Whitehurst junior around 1800 is shown in *Fig.* 49. The mahogany case is crisply carved with leaves with the stem joined by pierced leaf scrolls and capped by an urn. The silvered dial is signed 'Whitehurst, Derby' and is divided into hundredths of an inch. The set hand is adjusted by the brass knob to the right-hand side of the bezel. Like his uncle, John Whitehurst, he also made angle barometers.

During the second half of the

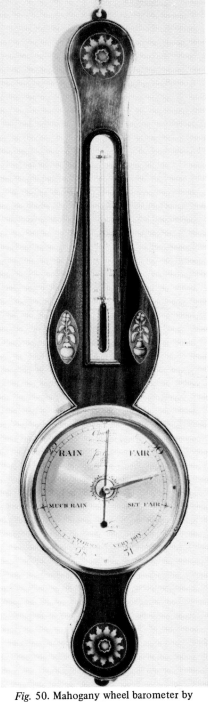

Fig. 50. Mahogany wheel barometer by James Gatty, c. 1790.

52

eighteenth century the stick barometer was still in vogue and it was not until the banjo-shaped wheel barometer was introduced to England, towards the end of the eighteenth century, that the wheel instrument was sold in substantial numbers. The banjo shape appears to have been brought from the continent by Italians who migrated from Holland and France around 1765. At that time there were quite a number of Italians established in these two countries as glassblowers and instrument makers, including barometers, having arrived in large numbers from Italy almost a hundred years earlier.

One of the earliest Italian immigrants was James Gatty who appears to have set up in business as a barometer maker at 130, High Holborn, London, at least by 1790. Besides making stick and multiple-tube barometers, he made a very large number of attractive and high-quality wheel barometers and, perhaps, did more than any other maker to popularise this type of barometer.

An example of his work is shown in *Fig.* 50. The pine case is veneered with mahogany and is outlined by triple stringing, with inlays of a floral paterae. A Fahrenheit alcohol thermometer has the four usual heat indications of Blood Heat, Summer Heat, Temperate and Freezing. The silvered brass dial is 8 inches in diameter and has horizontal weather indications, which was a feature on many of the earliest barometers, and the full dial allows a variation of 3 inches in the mercury – from 28 to 31. The indicating hand is made of blued steel, whilst the set hand, which is controlled by the knob fixed through the centre of the glass, is made of brass.

A contemporary of James Gatty was John Roncketi, another Italian immigrant who settled in England towards the end of the eighteenth century. He, too, made a large number of very fine barometers and was also described as an 'artificial flower and feather manufacturer'. He was established at 180, Holborn, London, between 1790 and 1797 and the barometer in *Fig.* 51 bears this address on the spirit level plate.

This round top design was the most popular until about 1810, but it is unusual for such an early wheel barometer to be fitted with a hygrometer and spirit level. The level was incorporated so that the barometer could be set up in an exactly vertical position, which is vital for an accurate reading, and also so that its position could be easily checked from time to time. The level plate was also used, particularly on later barometers, to engrave the maker's, or retailer's name, rather than on the main dial. As will be seen in succeeding illustrations, the level plates are almost invariably round or rectangular, an oval plate being very rare. The Dry/Moist hygrometer is adjustable by a cog mechanism operated by inserting a key just below the instrument. The same key is used to adjust the brass set hand which is connected by a pulley arrangement behind the dial to the key hole below the dial bezel. This arrangement for operating the set hand is always used when a convex glass is fitted to protect the dial. Adjustment by turning a knob fixed through the centre of the glass can only be used when the glass is flat, as in the James Gatty barometer, and is found only on early barometers.

Another unusual feature is the pointer to record thermometer readings; it is adjusted by a rack-and-pinion mechanism operated by the same key applied to the key hole below the thermometer. The mahogany case is slightly larger than for the standard 8 inch dial barometer, being 39 inches high and 2 inches in depth. The usual size is 36 inches high ahd 1½ inches in depth.

Broken-pediment wheel barometers were also made from about 1790 and the

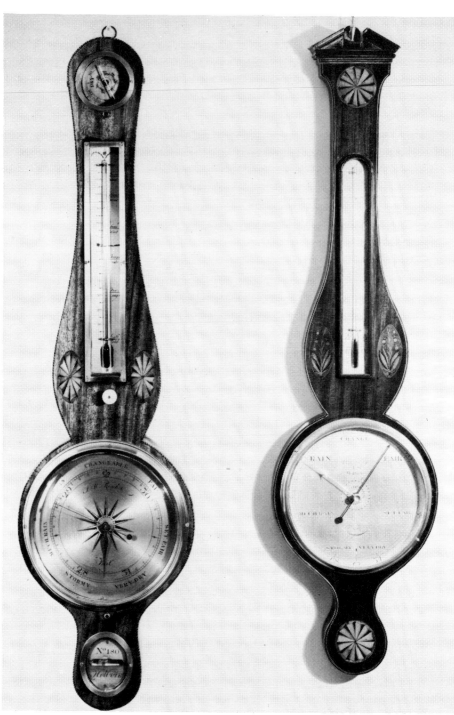

Fig. 51. Wheel barometer by J. M.
Roncketi, c. 1795.

Fig. 52. Broken-pediment wheel barometer by Lione & Co., c. 1800.

one shown in *Fig.* 52 can be dated c. 1800. The maker's name, 'Lione & Co., 81 Holborn, London', is engraved on the silvered brass dial, with all the weather indications horizontally placed. The barometer is very similar to the Gatty instrument already described, except that the round top has been replaced by a broken pediment. The side veneers of both barometers are laid across, rather than along, the length of the case, and this indicates that they are early barometers and of high quality.

The early makers generally used pine veneered with mahogany for the cases, but if they wished to make an exceptional barometer they were prepared to incur additional expense by using a satinwood veneer. An example can be seen in *Fig.* 53, with the case outlined with stringing and crossbanding. The Dry/Damp hygrometer is set in an unusual position, no doubt to maintain balance and symmetry, and some of the weather indications are again set horizontally. A dial of 10 inches in diameter is used and engraved with the maker's name, 'Anone, 26, High Holborn, London'. His Christian name was Francis and he operated from this address between 1802 and 1808, selling barometers, prints, telescopes and thermometers.

Another early unusual round top barometer is shown in *Fig.* 54. It is veneered in mahogany with zebra stringing and uncustomary paterae below the thermometer and the main dial. The Dry/Moist hygrometer is adjustable and the alcohol Fahrenheit thermometer plate has two additional heat indications of Fever Heat at 112 degrees and Extreme Cold at zero.

The 8 inch dial is engraved 'F. Amadio & Son, 118 St. John St. Road, London', and the traditional 3 inch scale is divided into twentieths of an inch. This graduation was commonly used on the dials of early round-top and broken-pediment barometers, although the scale was sometimes divided into fortieths or hundredths. Graduations of hundredths of an inch were not generally used until the scroll-pediment wheel barometer became popular around 1825, and as a general guide it can be stated that the later the barometer the more detailed the scale is likely to be. Francis Amadio is not recorded as having worked at 118, St. John Street Road until 1828, but various features of the barometer suggest that it was made not much later than 1800. It could be that an Amadio dial has been fitted to an earlier barometer, but this is unlikely as the engraving on the hygrometer plate is similar to that on the main dial, and both have similar type stars engraved in the centre of the dial.

Besides making barometers, Francis Amadio produced artificial flowers and philosophical instruments. The family must have been in business for many years, as the barometers in *Fig.* 67 (p. 67) and 70 (p. 70) were made at the same address between 1829 and 1844.

The scroll or swan-necked pediment, began to appear on wheel barometers from around 1805, but its use was generally confined to barometers with 10 or 12 inch dials and it was not until about 1825 that the scroll pediment became the standard design for all wheel barometers.

The 12 inch dial was the largest made for domestic use and an example is given in *Fig.* 55. The satinwood veneered case is approximately 45 inches high and is outlined with stringing and crossbanding in kingwood. The pediment has an ivory finial with two matching ivory rosettes at the top of each scroll. Convex glasses are fitted to all three brass bezels, but the mercury thermometer case has a flat glass. The complete thermometer case is detachable, by lowering a catch with the brass knob below the case, so that the thermometer can be used separately if required.

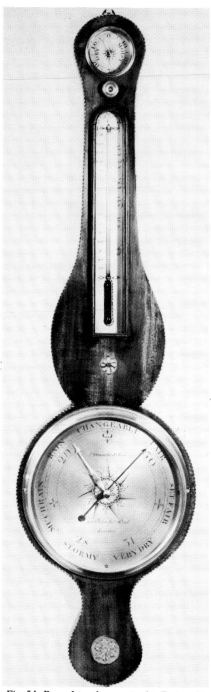

Fig. 53. Satinwood barometer by Francis Anone, c. 1805.

Fig. 54. Round-top barometer by F. Amadio & Son, c. 1805.

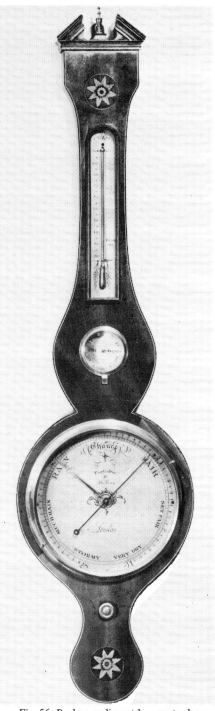

Fig. 55. Satinwood barometer by Tagliabue & Torre, c. 1805.

Fig. 56. Broken-pediment barometer by Tagliabue, c. 1810.

The spirit level plate is engraved with the maker's name, 'Tagliabue & Torre, 294 Holborn, London'. Caesar Tagliabue was trading from this address as an optician and barometer maker late in the eighteenth century, and took Torre into partnership around 1800. The partnership did not last for very long as Tagliabue was on his own again by 1807, working at 26, High Holborn, London, where he made the broken-pediment barometer with an 8 inch dial shown in *Fig.* 56 with detail in *Fig.* 57.

The mahogany case has ebony and boxwood stringing with flowerhead inlays at each end of the case. The hygrometer is set, unusually, in the centre of the case and the thermometer plate and dial engraving is particularly elaborate. Graduations on the dial are to the accuracy of one-fortieth of an inch and 'Tagliabue, 26, Holborn, London' is engraved. He also made the stick barometer shown in *Fig.* 17.

The changes in the style of engraving on wheel barometer dials followed, or were more or less in step with, the progressive alterations seen in the lettering on stick barometer register plates and noted in Chapter 2.

Round-top and broken-pediment wheel barometers made during the eighteenth and early nineteenth centuries were almost invariably engraved with Roman capitals for the weather indications, although Roman upper and lower case italics and copperplate script were occasionally used for the word Change. Upper and lower case italics and joined copperplate script were used for the thermometer scale wordings. Examples of both can be seen in *Figs.* 50, 54 and 62.

A Gothic style of lettering for the word Change appears to have been introduced on the scroll-pediment barometer when it became popular during the first quarter of the nineteenth century, and an example can be seen in *Fig.* 57. At the same time the Roman capitals used in Rain and Fair were emphasised by broadening them and accentuating the serifs. Rain and Fair or Stormy and Very Dry were occasionally engraved in the Gothic style. Except for the broken-pediment Sheraton shell barometer, which continued to have full Roman letters applied, the type of lettering shown in *Fig.* 57 was used on almost all types of wheel barometer until the third quarter of the nineteenth century, when the style of engraving shown in *Fig.* 76 (p.74) became popular. The main changes were that the Roman capitals for Rain and Fair became sanserif, and Stormy and Very Dry were engraved in the Gothic style. This mixed style of Roman and Gothic lettering continued to be used throughout the century and was also applied to aneroid barometer dials.

A particularly elegant 10 inch dial barometer with a broken pediment can be seen in *Fig.* 58. The dark mahogany case has crossbanding and satinwood stringing whilst the two scrolls of the pediment are also veneered with satinwood. It should be noticed that the vertical section of the case below the pediment is very short, extending to less than an inch, and this is a reliable indication of an early barometer; in fact, it is true to say that, generally, the shorter this section, the earlier the barometer is likely to be.

The maker's name, 'Charles Pitsalla, 221, High Holborn, London', is engraved on the spirit level plate. He was one of the early Italian immigrants and described as a weather-glass maker in the London trade directories around 1800. There is evidence that he was not averse to using second-hand materials, as the reverse side of the level plate is engraved 'A. Pizzala, London'.

Another scroll-pediment barometer with a 10 inch dial is illustrated in *Fig.* 59. The case is again veneered in mahogany with satinwood used to outline the frame

Fig. 57. Detail of *Fig.* 56.

Fig. 58. Scroll-pediment barometer by Charles Pitsalla, c. 1805.

Fig. 59. Mahogany clock barometer by Hudson, Greenwich, c. 1800.

and the clock and level bezels. The vertical section below the pediment is again very short, but a clock has replaced the standard hygrometer. Clocks began to appear occasionally on barometers from about 1800, but they were never adopted as a standard attachment. The clock has a fusee movement and was made by John Ward, 9 Fore Street, London, who is known to have worked at this address between 1784 and 1799. The maker of the barometer was Hudson of Greenwich whose name is engraved on the level plate. Very little is known of him, but the barometer must have been made around 1800.

Although scroll-pediment wheel barometers continued to be made by some makers during the first quarter of the nineteenth century, the majority produced were of the round-top or broken-pediment design. During this period the Italians continued to dominate the market and the barometers they produced were generally of a high quality.

An early Italian maker who favoured the broken pediment was Joseph Cetti who made a large number of barometers at London addresses between 1802 and 1839. He also made thermometers, looking-glasses and picture frames and, no doubt, his original trade was that of a glassblower.

An example of his early barometers is shown in *Fig.* 60 with the 8 inch dial engraved 'Cetti & Co., 54 Red Lion St., Holborne, London'. He is recorded as being at this address between 1803 and 1815 which dates the barometer to within twelve years. The barometer is similar in appearance to the one by Lione & Co. in *Fig.* 52 except that flowerhead inlays are used each side of the thermometer instead of a complete flower arrangement. The contrast can be more readily seen when compared with the James Gatty barometer in *Fig.* 50. The large shell inlay below the dial is an unusual feature, as it was the common practice for the inlay in this position to be the same as the one used below the pediment.

Joseph Cetti may well have been the first maker to introduce a shell inlay to the broken-pediment barometer and could probably claim responsibility for the barometer commonly known today as the Sheraton shell wheel barometer. Shell inlays, set each side of the thermometer case, began to appear around 1815 and this design of barometer remained the most popular until about 1825 when the scroll pediment became the standard feature. Cetti moved to 25, Red Lion Street, Holborn, in 1816, where he made 8 inch Sheraton shell followed by scroll-pediment barometers until 1839 when he handed over the business to his son John.

An example of the Sheraton shell barometer is shown in *Fig.* 61. It is very similar to the Cetti barometer just described, except that it has flowerhead inlays at each end of the mahogany case and shell inlays each side of the thermometer. The foliage, flower and shell motifs were derived from French decorative designs and were adapted by English furniture designers around 1750 and known as the 'French taste'. No doubt the Italian immigrants from France were used to this type of decoration and readily adapted it for barometers.

The 8 inch silvered dial is graduated to one twentieth of an inch and is engraved 'Trombetta'. The word 'Fecit' is added below the centre of the dial and this indicates that Trombetta made the barometer. This word appears on quite a number of early stick and wheel barometers, usually directly after the name engraved, and indicates that he was, in fact, the maker. The blued steel indicating hand with an arrow head and crescent tail was commonly used for dials until around 1825, although a frequent variation was a solid round tail. The brass recording hand is also typical of the same period, being solid with an arrow head. This type of

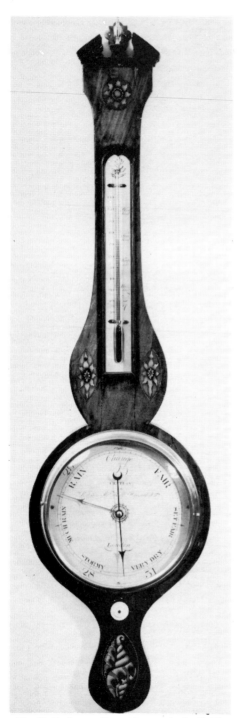

Fig. 60. Broken-pediment barometer by Cetti
& Co., c. 1810.

Fig. 61. Sheraton shell barometer by
Trombetta, c. 1820.

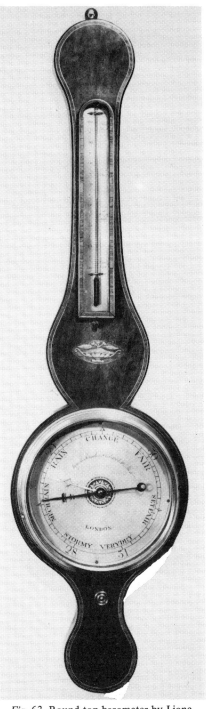

Fig. 62. Broken-pediment barometer by Lione & Somalvico, c. 1815.

Fig. 63. Round top barometer by Lione & Somalvico, c. 1815.

barometer was almost invariably veneered in mahogany with ebony and fruitwood stringing, although zebra stringing was sometimes used as an alternative. Another variation was the use of round shell inlays in place of the two flowerhead inlays.

There are still a very large number of 8 inch Sheraton shell barometers in existence, the majority of which would have been made between 1815 and 1825. The inlay patterns are achieved by using different coloured woods, with the edges singed to give the impression of shadow. No two barometers ever appear to be identical, particularly as regards the dials which are all engraved with differing central designs.

Not all of the Italian makers conformed to the shell and flowerhead inlay motifs, a notable exception being Lione & Somalvico, who were in partnership in Holborn, London, between 1805 and 1819. They preferred an inlay depicting an urn containing leaves and flowers and two of their barometers are shown in *Figs.* 62 and 63. They were both made about 1815 and serve to illustrate how varied were the barometers made even by one individual or firm. The broken-pediment barometer has ebony and pearwood stringing, a fixed thermometer case and a set hand operated through the centre of the glass dial; in contrast, the round-top example has ebony stringing and crossbanding, a removable thermometer case and a set hand operated by a pulley mechanism. The thermometer case has attractive matching crossbanding. The engraving on the dials and thermometer plates would appear to have been carried out by the same engraver, but there are still marked differences, whilst the dial hands are completely different.

Both dials are engraved: 'Lione & Somalvico, 14, Brook St., Holborn, London'. Dominick Lione and Joseph Somalvico are recorded as being at this address between 1811 and 1819 trading as opticians and barometer makers. During their partnership they made a large number of 8, 10 and 12 inch wheel barometers of mahogany or satinwood with round-top, broken or scroll pediments.

Of the fifteen wheel barometers already illustrated, and made between 1790 and 1820, it is significant that all except three of them were made by Italians. This suggests that they must have been responsible for popularising the wheel instrument and that they cornered the market for upwards of 30 years. By 1815 they were making large numbers to standard designs with specialist craftsmen making the various parts. To increase their sales they extended their outlets by selling wholesale to various retailers; the increased sales which resulted were at the expense of the stick barometer and this brought criticisms of the efficiency of the wheel instrument. The following is quoted from the Cyclopaedia in 1819:

> The wheel barometer has lately obtruded on the public by strolling Italian hawkers in our streets, but the imperfect manner in which these barometers are executed, as well as their defective principle, renders them mere mechanical pictures, and not scientific instruments, in the parlour.

No one would suggest that the wheel barometer is as accurate as its stick counterpart, but its sluggish mechanism has one marked advantage; tapping the dial will have the effect of bringing the reading up-to-date and the small adjustment seen in the indicating hand will show whether the pressure is rising or falling. Looking at the wheel barometers already illustrated, it is difficult to accept that they were 'executed in an imperfect manner' as, during the period covered, it is probably true to say that the best and most elegant instruments were made. The

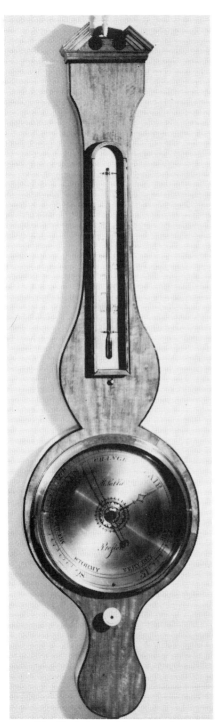 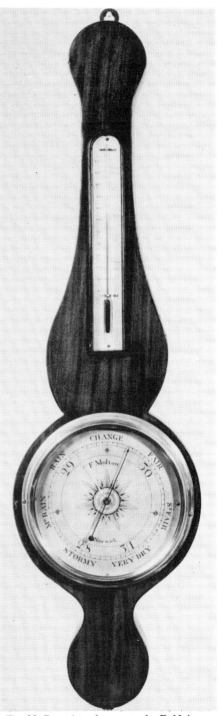

Fig. 64. Satinwood barometer by
M. Salla, Preston, c. 1815.

Fig. 65. Round-top barometer by F. Molton,
Norwich, c. 1815.

writer must surely have been referring to some inferior-quality barometers which did not stand the test of time. However, in spite of all the critics, the wheel barometer soon overtook the stick barometer in popularity in the home.

Although the cases were generally veneered with mahogany, more exotic woods, such as rosewood, maple, pearwood and satinwood were sometimes preferred. These woods were considered to be sufficient adornment in themselves so that the addition of inlays was not regarded as essential. *Fig.* 64 shows an 8 inch broken-pediment barometer with the case veneered in satinwood and outlined with ebony stringing, which is extended to the thermometer case. It was made by M. Salla of Preston about 1815 and the dial graduations are in fortieths of an inch.

Salla was one of the very few Italians working outside London during the first two decades of the nineteenth century. Others were Baptis Roncheti in Manchester, P. A. Tarone in Bristol and S. Bregazzi in Derby. The names of twelve Italians working in London during the same period have already been mentioned and to those can be added P. Barnarda, J. Corti, L. Martinelli, P. Manticha, F. Pastorelli, C. Stampa, A. Tarone and P. Gally who were all well-known barometer makers.

Mention should here be made of Francis Molton, one of the few Englishmen who made a large number of good-quality stick and wheel barometers in Norwich during the first quarter of the nineteenth century. *Fig.* 65 shows a mahogany 8 inch round-top barometer, with satinwood stringing, made about 1815. The brass bezel is fitted with a flat glass, but, at first sight, there is no visible means of adjusting the set hand. Molton appears to have adopted a unique method for making these adjustments; the brass key fitted below the case is connected by a cogged spindle which engages a cog-wheel that turns the set hand. Molton used this method on a number of his barometers, but no other maker appears to have adopted it.

Fig. 66 illustrates another round-top mahogany barometer by Francis Molton, made when he was working at 55, Lawrence Steps, Norwich, around 1820. He has used ebony and fruitwood stringing to line the case and both dials have one twentieth of an inch graduations. The two barometers again illustrate the individuality of each instrument, even when made by the same maker.

The swan-neck pediment became increasingly popular towards the end of the first quarter of the nineteenth century and was extended to the 8 inch dial barometers. An example is given in *Fig.* 67. The shell inlays have disappeared and the two flowerhead inlays have been replaced by a hygrometer and a spirit level, making a four dial barometer. The mahogany case is outlined with ebonised and fruitwood stringing and the hygrometer and thermometer can be detached and used separately. The main dial hand is similar to that used on the Sheraton shell barometer, but the brass set hand is pierced to form a pointer. The barometer was made c. 1830 by Francis Amadio of 118, St. John St. Road, London and his name and address is engraved on the dial. He also made the barometer in *Fig.* 54.

A clock barometer of the same period is shown in *Fig.* 68. It is almost 50 inches high, with a depth of almost 4 inches, and is veneered in rosewood. The main dial has a diameter of 12 inches and the hands were made to match the hands of the clock. The five dials are of silvered brass and, again, the hygrometer and bow-fronted thermometer case can be detached. The 8 day silent clock has a fusee movement.

Both barometer and clock were made by Santiago James Moore French of Royal Exchange, London, as evidenced by the engravings on the clock face and level plate. He was a member of the Clockmakers Company from 1810 to 1840 and was

Fig. 66. Round-top shell barometer by
F. Molton, Norwich, c. 1820.

Fig. 67. Scroll-pediment barometer by
F. Amadio, c. 1830.

67

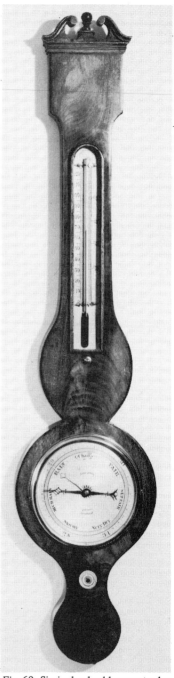

Fig. 69. Six inch wheel barometer by
Adie & Son, c. 1840.

Fig. 68. Rosewood clock barometer by
S. J. M. French, c. 1830.

noted for his chronometers, watches and barometers, some of which he sold abroad.

Other makers produced clock barometers of similar size, but they were usually veneered in mahogany with crossbanding of lighter woods and scroll pediments. The clocks were sometimes of the pendulum type.

The 12 inch dial barometer was the largest made for household use, although instruments of greater dimensions were made for halls, public buildings, institutions and for use out of doors. By way of contrast, a 6 inch dial barometer is shown in *Fig.* 69. The 37 inch high case is of mahogany with ebonised stringing and a wood finial. The makers name engraved is 'Adie & Son, Opticians, Edinburgh'. This was a partnership between Alexander Adie, who made the sympiesometer in *Fig.* 88, (p. 85), and his son Richard. They were in partnership from 1835 to 1858 when Alexander died.

A comparatively small number of 6 inch dial barometers were made and they are now valued more highly than the larger dial instruments. An even smaller number of 4½ inch dial barometers were produced, and one is shown in *Fig.* 70. This was the smallest wheel barometer made in commercial quantities and they are now classed as rare. The case is veneered in mahogany with no stringing, but the scroll pediment is decorated with ivory rosettes. This barometer, like the clock barometer by French, has more of a squared frame than the wheel instruments previously described and these features began to appear on scroll-pediment barometers from around 1820. The dial is calibrated to one hundredths of an inch and is engraved with the maker's name, 'F. Amadio & Son, 118, St. John St. Road, London'. He was a prolific maker and two of his barometers have already been described.

The barometer was made about 1840 and it was around this time that retailers began to have their names and addresses engraved on the spirit level plates. This probably explains why the retailers name, 'J. Mangiacavalli, 22, Charles St., Hatton Garden', is also engraved on the level plates. However, it was not usual for both the maker's and retailer's names to be engraved on a barometer, as the retailer wished to enhance his status by giving the impression that he was the maker.

A typical scroll-pediment barometer with a squared frame, which became popular about 1835, is illustrated in *Fig.* 71. The hygrometer and main 8 inch dial brass bezels are fitted with convex glasses and the detachable thermometer case has a bow front. The case is veneered with mahogany and outlined with a narrow multi-wood crossbanding edged with an ebony stringing. Both dial hands are pierced, the main hand being made of steel with a brass set hand. These types of hands began to be used from the 1830s and remained in general use until the late Victorian period. The maker's name, 'A. Gilardoni, Bristol', is engraved on the level plate.

A similar barometer, with a 12 inch dial, made by C. Maspolli, Manchester, around the same date of 1840, is shown in *Fig.* 72. The mahogany case is attractively crossbanded with satinwood and the quality of the instrument is emphasised by the very fine mother-of-pearl set hand key. The engraving on all four silvered brass dials is of a high quality, particularly the main dial, where Change is encircled by numerous swirls and flourishes and there is an elegant central design. Most engravers took great pride in adorning the centre of the main dial and a great variety of designs was used, including stars, geometric designs, floral patterns, windmills, birds and maps of the world.

These four dial barometers, with detachable thermometers and hygrometers were

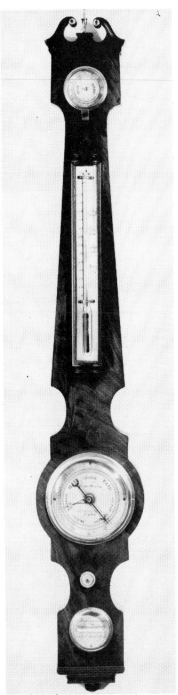

Fig. 70. Four and a half inch wheel barometer by F. Amadio & Son, c. 1840.

Fig. 71. Eight inch wheel barometer by A. Gilardino, c. 1840.

70

Fig. 72. Twelve inch wheel barometer by C. Maspolli, c. 1840.

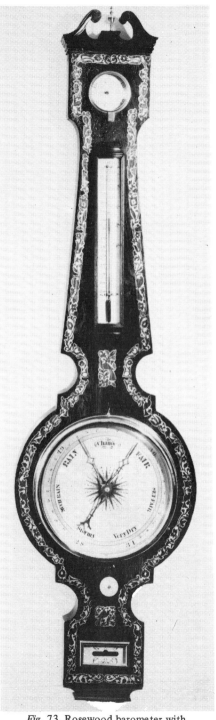

Fig. 73. Rosewood barometer with
mother-of-pearl inlay, c. 1840.

71

sometimes known as coach-house barometers as they were popular with landlords, and, during the early part of the nineteenth century, could be found in most inns and coaching houses. The thermometer would be placed on the mantelpiece of the inn bedroom and the hygrometer in the bed itself. If either reading was unsatisfactory to the guest the management were obliged to put some more fuel on the fire or the chambermaid would be sent up to put a copper warmingpan in the bed.

Decoration of the cases was not limited to stringing or crossbanding and other forms were used. A few barometers had cases outlined with a brass inlay, but a more common practice was to use a mother-of-pearl inlay.

A pattern comprising leaves, flowers and birds was the most popular and a standard composition can be seen on the barometer in *Fig. 73*. The case is veneered in rosewood and no fewer than 14 birds are outlined in mother-of-pearl. The construction of the barometer is identical to the two just described, except that the bow-fronted thermometer case is set flush against the case rather than set into it. Two screws are screwed almost full into the case and two holes are provided at the back of the thermometer case to receive the two screw heads. This method of attaching the thermometer was adopted around 1840 and avoids the use of a catch.

By 1845 the most popular design of wheel barometer was the five-face scroll-pediment type shown in *Fig. 74*. It is very similar to earlier barometers, except that the thermometer has been shortened so that a convex mirror could be incorporated above the main dial. Its purpose is not clear, but it certainly was not intended for use as a looking-glass; its main function appears to be decorative and to reflect the contents of the hall or room in which it was hung. The cases were veneered with mahogany or rosewood with stringing sometimes applied if mahogany was used. The 8 inch dial was the most popular, although 10 inch dials are common.

The maker of the example shown was John Schalfino, who was making barometers at East Street, Taunton, in the early 1840s. This barometer, and others made by him still extant, have masonic emblems engraved on the dials.

An historically interesting 10 inch barometer can be seen in *Fig. 75*. It is, very unusually, veneered with oak and was made by Mansford, London, c. 1840. Above the main dial is a small circular ivory plate on which is inscribed: 'Made from the wreck of the Royal George. Sunk August 29th 1782'.

The Royal George was a 100-gun flagship launched in 1757 and, whilst being heeled for underwater repairs, she overset and sank at her anchors in Portsmouth harbour. Rear Admiral Kempenfelt went down with her, together with about 900 other people, including many women and children. Her hulk became a shipping hazard and in 1817 an unsuccessful attempt was made to raise her; however, in 1839, quantities of gunpowder were used to blow up the ship and sections came to the surface. Using the old wood was a commercial way of commemorating the disaster – Cowper, the poet, was inspired to write the poem 'Toll for the Brave' and the elegy 'The Loss of the Royal George'.

The barometer is typical of the period and the design is very similar to the one by Shalfino, except that it has squared sections above and below the main dial. It also has a masonic symbol engraved about the central decoration (*see* detail in *Fig. 76*).

An unusual 8 inch dial barometer veneered in mahogany is shown in *Fig. 77*. It is similar in appearance to other barometers, but uses a very unusual system for recording the change in the mercury level. Instead of the standard pulley and glass weights to control the dial indicating hand, the maker has substituted a cog-wheel

Fig. 74. Mahogany five-dial barometer by J. Schalfino, c. 1845.

Fig. 75. Oak scroll-pediment barometer by Mansford, London, c. 1840.

73

Fig. 76. Detail of *Fig.* 75.

74

for the pulley which engages a toothed small brass bar connected to a cork resting on the mercury in the short tube. The cork floats on the mercury and as it rises and falls the bar is raised and lowered; this rotates the cog-wheel and so turns the indicating hand.

The maker was Watkins & Hill, 5 Charing Cross, London, and the barometer was made on 14 September 1848 and is numbered 201. All this information is engraved on the dial together with 'Registered — 1586'. Where the cog and engaging tooth invention was registered is not clear, but it does not appear to have been registered at the Patent Office. However, Watkins & Hill seem to be the only maker who adopted this system, which does not seem to operate as efficiently as the pulley and glass weights mechanism.

The Watkins & Hill partnership was formed in 1819 and was taken over by Elliott Bros. in 1857. Jeremiah Watkins, the senior partner, was the nephew of Francis Watkins who made the calendar barometer in *Fig.* 14.

The scroll-pediment design of case remained popular until well into the third quarter of the nineteenth century and was made with a mahogany or rosewood frame. Other designs appeared from time to time, and one which was produced about 1850 and increased in popularity is shown in *Fig.* 78. It is now known as the onion-top or tulip-top banjo barometer, because of its shape, and very many can still be seen in antique shops with cases usually veneered with rosewood, although sometimes mahogany was used with a boxwood stringing.

The one illustrated has a rosewood veneer with an alcohol thermometer and Fahrenheit scale. The 8 inch dial is graduated in hundredths of an inch and the name 'Chick, Worthing' is engraved. 'Warranted Correct' is engraved on the spirit level plate and this was a common practice when the maker's or retailer's name was engraved on the main dial.

These barometers were produced with or without a mirror, and one without a mirror is shown in *Fig.* 79. The case is veneered with rosewood and is painted to resemble stringing and brass or mother-of-pearl inlay, which was a feature of some of the more expensive barometers. 'P. Bragonzi, Hereford' is engraved on the level plate and he.was probably the retailer. Italian names are engraved on the majority of barometers made between 1790 and 1850, and it has been suggested that such was the popularity of barometers made by the Italians that some English makers and retailers had Italian names engraved on them so that they would sell more readily.

During the 1850s the design of the case changed progressively and *Fig.* 80 shows a rosewood barometer made early in that decade. By way of decoration eight round scrolls have been added to the case with each scroll inlaid with mother-of-pearl circles and a star. The retailer was F. H. Hallett of Trowbridge in Wiltshire.

This type of barometer had an 8 or 10 inch silvered brass dial and was sometimes veneered with mahogany; a detachable thermometer was always fitted, but not all had a hygrometer and a spirit level.

The most expensive type of wheel barometer made during this period is illustrated in *Fig.* 81. The best rosewood frame is elegantly inlaid with variegated buhl work of mother-of-pearl and gold depicting birds, flowers, buds and leaves, with the Prince of Wales Feathers above the 8 inch silvered brass dial. The maker's name, 'P. Mantova, Luton', is engraved on the dial.

Barometers of this quality were made with 10, 12 and 14 inch dials, the latter being suitable for mansions, clubs and halls etc. Brass was generally used rather than

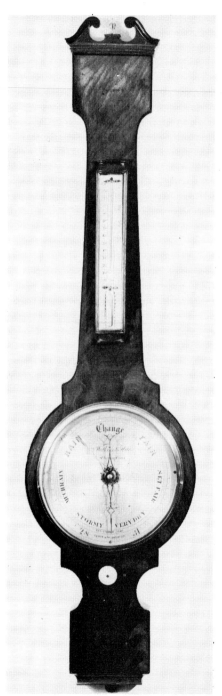

Fig. 77. Mahogany scroll-pediment barometer by Watkins & Hill, c. 1848.

Fig. 78. Rosewood onion-top barometer
by Chick, Worthing, c. 1850.

76

Fig. 79. Rosewood tulip-top barometer by P. Bragonzi, c. 1850.

Fig. 80. Rosewood banjo barometer by F. H. Hallett, c. 1855.

gold and the 12 and 14 inch instruments usually incorporated an 8 day pendulum clock between the dial and the thermometer – they were advertised for sale at £20 in 1860.

Towards the end of the 1850s the pointed features of the onion- or tulip-top case were being replaced by the scroll-pattern barometers with round moulded edges. They were still veneered with mahogany or rosewood, with a silvered brass dial and detachable Fahrenheit thermometer which also sometimes had a centigrade scale. The use of a spirit level was becoming less common and the oat beard hygrometer was being abandoned in favour of the wet and dry bulb hygrometer, which was found to be more efficient and was used as a separate instrument.

Fig. 82 shows this design of barometer which was commonly on sale around 1860. The majority produced had plain veneered cases, but the particular example has the best-quality rosewood case which is inlaid with variegated pearl, tortoise shell and brass to make four attractive and colourful scenes. The raised carving at the bottom of the case was a common feature on barometers made between 1855 and 1875. The 8 inch dial is engraved 'Gardner & Co. 21 Buchanan St. Glasgow', and the firm is recorded as operating from this address between 1839 and 1860 as opticians and mathematical instrument makers. A large family of Gardners were active at various addresses in Glasgow between 1765 and 1860, during which time they produced very many high-quality stick and wheel barometers.

A similar 10 inch dial barometer, made about 5 years later, is shown in *Fig.* 83. The rosewood case is decorated with mother-of-pearl inlays and the only change in the shape of the case is the section below the dial which has become less rounded. It will be seen that the Fahrenheit mercury thermometer case has a flat front with a flat glass, and it was around 1865 that the more expensive bow-fronted case ceased to be used. The maker was Hodson of Worcester.

The majority of these barometers had plain mahogany or rosewood veneered cases with silvered brass dials, but some were made with porcelain dials with black enamel figures and divisions; a few dials were made of enamelled metal. All had brass bezels fitted with a convex glass. Instruments intended for sale abroad were fitted with a steel or glass stopcock which was found to be more satisfactory than plugging the tube.

Fig. 84 illustrates an 8 inch dial barometer made about 1870 by 'Negretti & Zambra, Instrument Makers to Her Majesty, London'. The case is veneered in walnut and the round moulded edging is restricted to the sides of the case. This type of barometer was occasionally fitted with two brass set hands with 'A. M. Today' engraved on one and 'P. M. Today' on the other, so that comparisons could be made. The hands were controlled by two keys set below the dial.

Later barometers had plain cases with no moulding whilst some cases were made of solid rosewood, walnut, mahogany or oak and elegantly carved to any style of furniture or architecture, for halls, libraries etc. The solid wood carved cases showed something of the Gothic or Medieval influence and elaborate floral designs were also carved on the banjo-type frames.

Fig. 85 shows a solid oak barometer made around 1860 by Marratt of King William Street, London Bridge. The case is quite heavily carved, but not unattractive, although this cannot be said of all the barometers made in the second half of the nineteenth century. The 10 inch dial is divided into hundredths of an inch and the detachable thermometer carries Fahrenheit and Reaumur scales.

The later a barometer was made in the nineteenth century the more likely it was

Fig. 81. Rosewood inlaid barometer by
P. Mantova, c. 1855. (Reproduced by
kind permission of M. W. Cox, Esq.)

Fig. 82. Eight inch wheel inlaid barometer
by Gardner & Co., c. 1860.

79

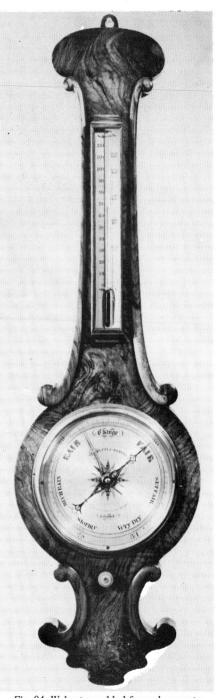

Fig. 83. Ten inch wheel inlaid barometer
by Hodson, Worcester, c. 1865.

Fig. 84. Walnut moulded frame barometer
by Negretti & Zambra, c. 1870.

80

to be inelegant and over-ornate, this being mainly the result of the use of mass-production methods. They were heavily fashioned, usually in solid oak, with moulded edges, and because of their carved scrolls continued to be called the 'Scroll Pattern'.

The popularity of the aneroid barometer increased dramatically during the second half of the nineteenth century with the result that far fewer wheel barometers were produced. A negligible number were made in the twentieth century and, in fact, between 1919 and 1925 reproduction broken-pediment and scroll-pediment wheel barometers began to appear.

Fig. 85. Oak carved barometer by Marratt, London Bridge, c. 1860.

6 Other Mercurial and Liquid Barometers

The early weather-glasses contained water and were in use before the Torricelli experiment in 1643. An old Dutch weather-glass is shown in *Fig.* 86. They were made in this form from early in the seventeenth century to 1939 and are known in Holland as the 'Donderglas', meaning the thunder glass, as thunder could be expected when water dripped from the spout. An example can be seen in the Science Museum, London.

It is similar to a coffee pot with a sealed lid, so that the water has to be introduced through the spout. There is, of course, air in the glass above the water and the glass is set up by arranging for the level of the water in the spout to be equal to the level of the water in the glass when the atmospheric pressure is normal or average i.e. when a mercury barometer is reading 29·5 inches.

The atmospheric pressure of the air in the glass remains relatively constant, so that when the outside atmospheric pressure increases, the level of the water in the spout will fall, whilst the reverse will apply when the outside atmospheric pressure is less than that of the air in the glass. The disadvantage of this type of weather glass is that the water is also affected by temperature, so that when the temperature increases, the water expands and rises in the spout; similarly, when the temperature decreases the water contracts and falls in the spout. It is, therefore, essential for this type of weather glass to be maintained in a constant temperature.

Various attempts have been made, in the seventeenth century and later, to improve the portability of the mercury barometer by reducing its size. With this in mind, Guillaume Amontons in 1688 suggested splitting the height of the mercury column by joining together several parallel tubes and filling them alternately with mercury and a lighter liquid.

This design was followed by a number of makers, including James Gatty and Bapt. Roncheti mentioned earlier, and became known as a double- or multiple-tube barometer. An example by Rabalio, which can be dated about 1790, is shown in *Fig.* 87. The case is made of mahogany with a glazed door; the three finials are of brass and the thermometer scales and weather indications are stamped on a box-wood base. Mercury and oil are used alternately in the tube and the level of the oil in the open right-hand side tube indicates the atmospheric pressure; the lower the pressure the higher the oil rises in the tube. The barometer is approximately 24 inches high and by using oil in conjunction with mercury it was possible to extend the scale to 15 inches as against 3 inches for the normal stick barometer. The set hand slides up and down a brass wire which is secured at the top and bottom of the door frame.

This type of barometer never became popular and was made for only a very limited period, the main disadvantages being that the liquids could easily become intermingled when the barometer was carried or shaken, the tubes also became stained and are difficult to clean.

A similar type of instrument called a sympiesometer was invented and patented in 1818 by Alexander Adie (1774–1858). Adie was an optician and traded from

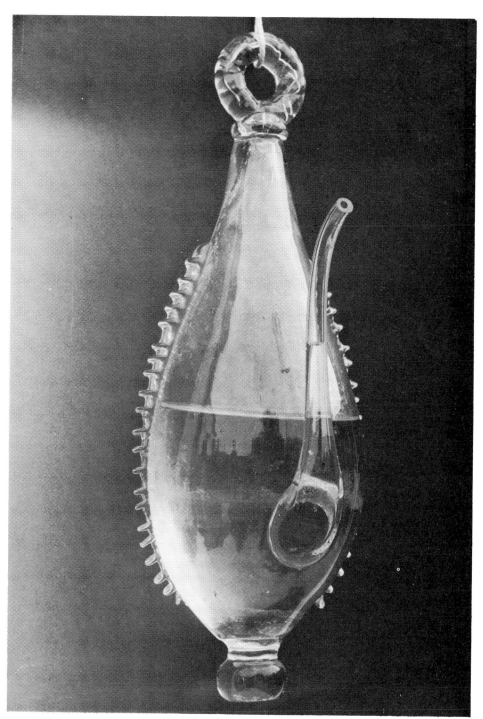

Fig. 86. Old Dutch weather-glass.

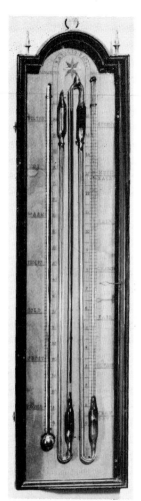

Fig. 87. Double- or multiple-tube barometer by Rabalio, c. 1790.

various addresses in Edinburgh; he also made domestic and marine barometers. It appears that he numbered his sympiesometers, and the one illustrated in *Fig.* 88 is engraved 'Patent A. Adie Edinburgh No. 537'. The case is of mahogany with a glazed door and the height is a little over 24 inches. The top part of the tube, including the closed bulb, is filled with hydrogen, whilst the lower part of the tube and the open bulb contains a coloured almond oil. There is a fixed scale of temperatures on the extreme right of the case and a scale of pressures is made to slide against it. A similar instrument inscribed 'Patent. Adie & Son. Edinburgh No. 1393' is on view in the Science Museum, London. Also on view is one by Louis Casella, maker of the agricultural barometer described later. There are also two sympiesometers in the University of Oxford Museum of History of Science; both are made by Adie & Son and numbered 2085 and 2154, which suggests that 10,000 could have been made in the second quarter of the nineteenth century.

As hydrogen is affected by both pressure and temperature of the atmosphere, it is necessary to adjust for the temperature when taking a reading. To take a reading, the thermometer is first read and an index mark on the scale of pressures – in this case adjacent to the 31 inches mark – is set opposite the reading on the fixed scale of temperatures by raising or lowering the sliding scale with the brass knob outside the case. The pressure is then read from the sliding scale opposite the level of the oil in the tube. There is a circular recording dial at the bottom of the case.

The advantage of the sympiesometer was that it was smaller and simpler than the mercury barometer. It was developed primarily by Adie to replace the marine barometer and he arranged for it to be tested extensively on board ship, both in tropical and arctic conditions, before applying for a patent. It was then declared superior in all respects to the marine barometer. Because of its extreme sensibility and convenient size it was often used for marine observations, but by 1885 it was only rarely used owing to the ease with which it could be put out of adjustment when being moved. However, it was still used for the purposes of comparison and sometimes mounted on the cases of marine barometers in place of a thermometer, until it was finally replaced by the aneroid barometer.

The size of sympiesometer varied between 6 and 24 inches in height depending on the purpose for which the instrument was required; the smallest was the pocket sympiesometer which was sometimes fitted with ivory scales and protected by a neat velvet-lined pasteboard or morocco case. *Fig.* 89 shows an 'Improved Sympiesometer' made around 1840 by J. Hughes of Ratcliff, London. The frame is of mahogany and of similar size to the Adie instrument just described, but in this case the upper portion of the tube is filled with air, whilst the lower portion and

part of the cistern is filled with sulphuric acid, coloured to make it visible. The cistern is open at the top through a kind of pipette or cone, and a brass cover prevents dust and dirt from entering. The adjustable scale of pressures is mounted over a fixed scale of temperatures, and before a reading is taken the pointer attached to the top of the pressure scale is adjusted to the appropriate temperature by the ivory key fixed half way down the right-hand side of the case. This particular sympiesometer was made for use at sea and has a contraction in the liquid column opposite the cistern to prevent violent oscillation of the liquid.

Although the barometer as a scientific instrument is outside the scope of this book, mention should be made of the Standard or Fortin type barometer suggested by Nicolas Fortin (1750–1831). Barometers were made for scientists long before they were made for domestic use, but it was not until 1810 that Fortin suggested combining a glass cistern with a leather base and an ivory point to determine the zero of the scale.

Such a barometer is shown in *Fig.* 90. It was made about 1820 by Chancellor & Son, 55 Lower Sackville Street, Dublin, who were notable clockmakers early in the nineteenth century. The circular metal case is painted black, with brass rings and screws, with the cistern formed from a glass cylinder so that the mercury inside can be seen. A conical piece of ivory is fixed to the top of the inside of the cistern with the point of the cone facing downwards. The point is set to coincide exactly with the zero of the scale and before taking a reading the mercury in the cistern is raised or lowered by the adjustable screw operating against a leather base, until it just touches the point of the ivory. This system allows very accurate readings to be taken and was adopted and retained with little alteration for a hundred and fifty years.

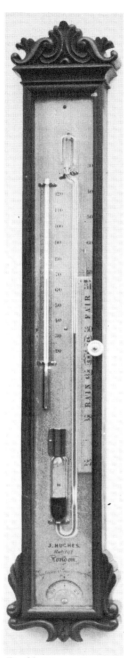

Fig. 89. Improved sympiesometer by J. Hughes, London, c. 1840.

Fig. 88. Sympiesometer by A. Adie, Edinburgh, c. 1825.

85

The upper end of the protective case has two vertical openings opposite each other so that readings can be taken and aided by light reflected from the white opaque glass reflector let into the mahogany board on which the barometer is mounted. There is also a similar reflector behind the glass cistern so that the mercury can be adjusted accurately. The vernier allows a reading to the accuracy of one five-hundredth of an inch and the scale extends from 27 to 33 inches. The mercury thermometer has a Fahrenheit scale and there is a hole in the case under the thermometer bulb so that it can record more accurately the mercury temperature.

These barometers were used mainly for scientific purposes and by observatories and meteorological stations throughout the world.

Mountain or traveller's barometers were also made using the Fortin principle, but they were much reduced in size and weight. Their appearance was similar except that the scale was graduated from 32 inches to 14 inches. The barometer was sold with a portable brass tripod stand and gimbal to allow it to revolve, packed in a leather sling case, metal lined for travelling.

Siphon tube mountain barometers were also made on the Gay-Lussac (q.v.) principle. In this design the short limb of the tube was sealed at the top, after the mercury had been introduced, and a small hole was made, an inch or so below the seal, which was covered with a substance which allowed the access of air but prevented the escape of mercury when the barometer was packed for travelling. The bent part of the tube was contracted to a capillary bore so that when the barometer was inverted the capillary attraction kept the mercury in the long limb. A Bunten air trap was fitted in the lower end of the long limb to prevent any air rising to the vacuum. The metal tube protecting the glass was graduated from

Fig. 90. Fortin barometer by Chancellor & Son, Dublin, c. 1820.

Fig. 91. Mountain station or balloonist barometer by H. Negretti, c. 1845.

the centre and readings were taken from two verniers, one positioned at the top of the mercury in the long limb and the other at the top of the mercury in the short limb. The sum of the two readings gave the correct height of the mercury to one five-hundredth of an inch. These instruments also had tripod stands and travelling cases.

J. L. Gay-Lussac (1778–1850) was a famous French chemist who favoured the siphon tube barometer, rather than the cistern tube, as it did not require a correction for capillary attraction. In 1816 he improved the performance of the siphon tune, as already described, and for the following 30 years it was popular with travellers because it was light and compact.

Fig. 91 shows a mountain station or balloonist's barometer by H. Negretti, which uses a Gay-Lussac type tube. It has an ivory scale which is calibrated from 31 inches to 5 inches and can be adjusted by turning the ivory circular key half way up the tube. This is necessary to zero the scale by ensuring that the brass arm, connected by a brass rod to the bottom of the scale, is level with the top of the mercury in the short limb. The bulge in the lower section of the long limb contains a Bunten air trap. The case is made of mahogany with a glazed door and the maker's name, 'H. Negretti, 19 Leather Lane, Holborn', is engraved at the top of the scale. As he only occupied these premises from 1843 to 1848, the barometer can be dated within 5 years. Negretti came to England in 1830 at the age of 12 and was apprenticed in 1838 to F. A. Pizzala, an optician, instrument and barometer maker. He was in business on his own account by 1840 but formed a partnership with J. W. Zambra in 1850.

This instrument could have been used as a mountain station barometer or, perhaps, in early balloon experiments, since Henry Negretti was an acquaintance of James Glaisher the well-known balloon pioneer who was a Fellow of the Royal Society and one-time Secretary of the British Meteorological Society.

Mention should here be made of the Newman's mountain barometer which was developed by John Newman in 1833 and was a successful portable barometer for use at high altitudes. The round frame was made of wood or brass with a brass shield that would slide round to protect the scales when in transit. A thermometer was mounted on the long scale which could be read down to 18 inches and a vernier screw was operated from the top of the barometer. Some barometers have the thermometer mounted just above the brass cistern cover. An ingenious method was employed to make the barometer portable; the bottom section of the cistern could be rotated, after inclining the instrument, and this disconnected a tube joining an upper and a lower section of the cistern, and so cut off the mercury. On the frame were pasted instructions for corrections of capacities, neutral point, capillary action and temperature.

John Newman was an important barometer maker between 1817 and 1862, trading from 7 & 8 Lisle Street, Leicester Square, 109 Regent Street and 122 Regent Street, London. He made the Royal Society's standard barometer and supplied those taken on the Ross Antarctic expedition.

By the middle of the nineteenth century there was a very large number of barometer makers and competition was severe. Factory methods were used for their production and in an endeavour to increase sales some makers began to make barometers for specific purposes.

In 1857 an agricultural or cottage barometer was marketed by L. Casella, and one is shown in *Fig.* 92. It was expressly designed by Casella as a cheap, light and

Fig. 92. Agricultural or cottage barometer by L. Casella, London, c. 1860.

portable barometer for use in cottages, garden sheds, greenhouses and farm buildings. It is made of solid mahogany with printed paper plates protected by glass. The standard weather indications are used and below them is the word 'Compensating'. This indicates that the inch calibrations on the register plates are, in fact, slightly less than inches, to compensate for the slight rise and fall in the level of the mercury in the bulb cistern, as the height of the mercury ranges between 26 and 31 inches on the scale.

It can be confidently stated that this type of barometer was introduced in 1857, as *The Field*, published on the 7 November 1857, commented:

> Casella's cottage barometer has lately been brought under our notice, very much to our delight and profit. They have registered with unerring faithfulness the recent changes in the weather.

In the *Cottage Gardener* of the 27 October 1857, the following testimonial was written:

> ... would adorn alike the gardener's cottage or the hall of the mansion. We are much obliged to Mr. Casella for thus popularizing these useful instruments. His name is a guarantee for the character of any instrument.

The following printed 'Instructions and Remarks' on the back of the barometer are still legible and worth repeating:

> In placing the Agricultural Barometer a shaded position is the best. The words Rain, Change, Fair, etc. are of less moment than the Figures; thus 29½, or Change, is considered about the Mean or Point leading to a change of weather and a rise of the mercury to ½ an inch above this point, or a fall of a ¼ of an inch below, is generally succeeded by decidedly Dry or Wet weather. In this country the mercury seldom rises higher than 30½ inches, or falls below 28. A gradual Rise or Fall of the mercury, indicates greater change than sudden fluctuations. Where the state of the weather appears to disagree with any great change of the barometer, such change may be looked for with double force with no great distance off. Thus, in May 1857, in and around London, the mercury which had been lowering for some days, began to rise with but ¾ of an inch of rain, whilst Reading, in Berkshire, only thirty miles off, was visited by a storm so severe as almost to form an event in the annals of the town. The following remarks of the learned Dr. Halley ('Philosophical Transactions' No. 187) will be found useful and interesting: 1st. In calm weather, when the air is inclined

Fig. 93. Cottage barometer by Langford, Bristol, c. 1865.

to rain the mercury is commonly low. 2nd. It is generally high in good, serene, settled fair weather. 3rd. It sinks lowest of all in very great winds, though not attended with rain. 4th. The greatest height of the mercury is observed when an easterly or northerly wind prevails. 5th. In calm frosty weather, the mercury is in general high. 6th. After very great storms of wind, when the mercury has been low, it usually rises again very fast. 7th. More northerly places have a greater alteration of the rise and fall of the mercury than the more southerly. 8th. Within the tropics, and near them, the changes and alterations in the weather make little or no variation in the height of the mercury. For instance, at Naples, it hardly ever exceeds an inch; whereas at Upminster, Dr. Dereham informs us, there is a difference of two and a half inches and at Petersburgh 3.31 inches'.

The words 'Agricultural Barometer' are printed above the maker's name, 'L. Casella, London'. He was mentioned earlier in connection with the stick barometer by C. Tagliabue shown in *Fig.* 17. He married Tagliabue's eldest daughter in 1837 and was taken into partnership a year later. The firm traded as Louis Casella & Company between 1848 and 1860 and were instrument makers to the Admiralty and the Board of Trade; they also supplied the American Government and the East India Company. The business continues today under the name of C. F. Casella & Co. Ltd.

A country-made bulb cistern cottage barometer by Langford of Bristol is illustrated in *Fig.* 93. The case is of solid oak and the design very similar to the Casella agricultural barometer just described; in fact it is suspected that Langford read the 'Instructions and Remarks' on the back of Cassella's barometer – particularly the suggested maximum variations in pressure in England – as he limited his scale from 27½ inches to 31 inches. The register plates and name plate are of ivory and the thermometer has a Fahrenheit scale.

A William Langford is recorded as having worked in Bristol as a watch and clockmaker from 1825 and he, or his son, could well have been the maker about 1865.

Louis Casella was not allowed to dominate the field for long with his agricultural barometer, as around 1860 a farmer's barometer was produced which incorporated a hygrometer to ascertain the humidity of the atmosphere.

It had been recognised since Dr Robert Hooke made the first oat beard hygrometer in England in 1663 that changes in air pressures were brought about by a change in wind speed as well as by rain, and one criticism of the simple barometer was that it was difficult to determine whether to expect rain or wind when the mercury began to fall. With the addition of a hygrometer this uncertainty could be removed. An oat beard in a hygrometer has only a very limited effective life and it was considered that the farmer, who needed more than most people to be able to forecast the weather accurately, should have a more reliable and scientific instrument.

This took the form of a wet and dry bulb hygrometer, and one is incorporated in the farmer's barometer shown in *Fig.* 94. It consists of two Fahrenheit thermometers set on the ivory register plates, one being each side of the tube. The bulb of the thermometer on the left-hand plate is exposed and records the temperature of the surrounding air. The bulb of the thermometer on the right-hand side plate is covered with a piece of muslin which is attached to some lamp-wick cotton, the ends of which are immersed in water in a small container which is fixed just below the thermometer. The water rises to the muslin by capillary action and keeps the thermometer bulb moist. The humidity of the air is obtained by taking a reading from each thermometer and noting the difference between them. The wet bulb thermometer will always be found to give a lower reading than the dry bulb thermometer and the greater the difference between them the lesser the amount of moisture in the air.

The evaporation of the water in the muslin round the bulb is a continuous process and this causes the temperature of the muslin to fall below that of the surrounding air. As the muslin is in contact with the thermometer bulb it will, of course, lower its temperature. A difference of 5 to 8 degrees was considered to indicate a healthy amount of moisture in the air of a living-room.

Negretti & Zambra were early makers of farmer's barometers and they drew up some rules to assist farmers in interpreting the various indications which the barometer gave, pointing out that account must also be taken of the force and direction of the wind, the nature of any particular season and the time of year.

Rules for Foretelling the Weather
A Rising Barometer
A 'Rapid' rise indicates unsettled weather.

A 'Gradual' rise indicates settled weather.

A 'Rise', with dry air, and cold increasing in summer, indicates wind from northward; and if rain has fallen, better weather is to be expected.

A 'Rise', with moist air and a low temperature, indicates wind and rain from northward.

A 'Rise', with southerly wind, indicates fine weather.
A Steady Barometer
With dry air and a seasonable temperature, indicates a continuance of very fine weather.
A Falling Barometer
A 'Rapid' fall indicates stormy weather.

A 'Rapid' fall, with westerly wind, indicates stormy weather from northward.

A 'Fall' with a northerly wind, indicates storm, with rain and hail in summer, and snow in winter.

A 'Fall', with increased moisture in the air, and the heat increasing, indicates wind and rain from southward.

A 'Fall', with dry air, and cold increasing (in winter), indicates snow.

A 'Fall', after very calm and warm weather, indicates rain with squally weather.

For the hygrometer to work efficiently it was essential for the barometer to be

set up in a position sufficiently exposed to the external air. If, for any reason, this was not practicable, a separate hygrometer could be purchased. Some time later a set of tables was produced giving the value of hygrometric readings in a simple form for use of the ordinary observer.

The farmer's barometer in *Fig.* 94 was made or retailed by W. E. Perrett of Weston-super-Mare about 1865. It has a solid oak frame with a cistern tube and portable screw. There is a sliding vernier and Fitzroy's weather indications are used. This type of barometer was made for about 50 years; they all appear to have had oak frames, but some were more elaborate than the one described, having carved oak frames and ornamental mountings. The register plates were made of ivory or were enamelled.

Early in the 1860s it was realised that a barometer would be of assistance in the management of mines, as explosions of gas in coal mines often occurred when the barometer reading was low. The inflammable and suffocating gases found in coal mines are heavier than air and tend to emerge from the least ventilated galleries when there is a fall in air pressure. The pressure of the atmosphere also plays an important part upon the liberation of gas from coal seams and fissures. When the barometer is high the gas is held in check within the coal and a sudden fall in air pressure will release it.

Barometers made specifically for miners, called miner's or pit barometers, were on sale certainly before 1864, but it was not until 1872 that an Act of Parliament was passed making the use of a barometer compulsory. Accurate records were maintained from the barometers previously in use and it was shown that before an explosion in a coal mine there was a diminution of atmospheric pressure. The government of the day was so convinced of the advantages in using a barometer in mines that when passing the 'Mines (Coal) Regulations Act

Fig. 94. Farmer's barometer by W. E. Perrett, Weston-super-Mare, c. 1865.

Fig. 95. Miner's barometer by J. Davis & Son, c. 1875.

1872' – 'An Act to consolidate and amend the Acts relating to the Regulation of Coal Mines and certain other Mines' – the following Section 26 was included: 'After dangerous gas has been found in any mine, a barometer and thermometer shall be placed above ground in a conspicuous position near the entrance to the mine.'

Although the Act only referred to a barometer for use above ground they were, in fact, all of robust construction so that they could also be used underground. All the barometers made were of very similar design and *Fig.* 95 shows a standard type by J. Davis & Son of London and Derby. It has a solid oak frame with a glass face framed in bronze metal. The aslant register plates are of ivory and are calibrated from 26 to 33 inches to allow the barometer to be used at least 2,000 feet below sea level. A cistern tube is used and for accuracy the scale is compensated or corrected for capacity. A single vernier is fitted and adjusted by the key below the face, through a rack-and-pinion mechanism. The mercury thermometer has a Fahrenheit scale but, understandably, there are no weather indications on the register plates, as the prime objective was to give warning of low air pressures.

Some pit barometers had metal or enamel plates and some were calibrated up to 34 inches. Others had an india-rubber bag over the cistern, with the brasswork and cistern coated with marine glue to prevent moisture penetrating. These types of barometer were made until 1930 with very little alteration.

An unusual barometer is shown in *Fig.* 96. It is, in effect, a stick and a wheel barometer combined in one instrument, but why it was made is difficult to judge. The case is of solid oak with the pediment again a combination of those seen on wheel and stick barometers; the square moulded centre section above the register plates was commonly seen on stick barometers from 1815, whilst the scrolls or swan necks which flank the centre section were very common on wheel barometers from the same period. The centre 8 inch dial has a convex glass and bow glass is used to protect the thermometer and register plates. The thermometer case is detachable and an unusual feature is that the thermometer has Fahrenheit, Raeumur and centigrade scales.

A siphon-type tube is fitted and use is made of the level of the mercury in the long and short arms to record the individual barometer readings, the systems adopted being identical to those used in stick and wheel barometers. However, because the bore of the short tube is little more than twice the bore of the long tube, the register plate calibrations had to be compensated to the extent that the mercury has only to rise by 2¾ inches to cover the full 4 inch calibrated scale.

The barometer was made by N. Whitehouse of 2, Cranbourn Street, Leicester Square, London, and can be dated c. 1840. There seems little advantage in arranging two readings from the same tube, as any fault or air lock in the tube will affect both readings. A better arrangement would have been to fit two tubes, when true comparisons could have been made.

Another uncommon design of wheel barometer is shown in *Fig.* 97, which can be dated about 1835. The mechanism is the same as in an ordinary siphon tube wheel barometer, except that the thread connecting the pulley to the glass weights is some 22 inches in length. A limited number of these barometers was made and they all had a flat rectangular mirror above the spirit level. This design was, no doubt, prompted by a desire to make it possible to use the mirror as a looking-glass; the barometer was usually hung in the hall and the lady of the house, and visitors, could check their appearance on entering and before leaving.

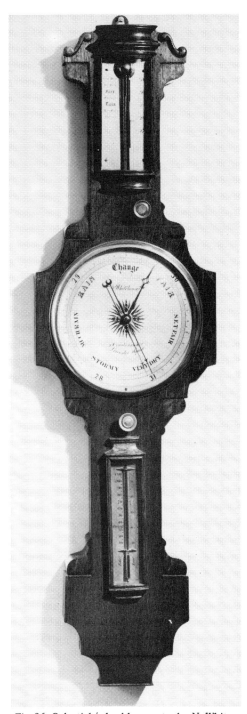

Fig. 96. Oak stick/wheel barometer by N. White-house, London, c. 1840.

Fig. 97. Mahogany wheel barometer by J. Laffrancho, Ludlow, c. 1835.

93

Fig. 98. Admiral Fitzroy's barometer, c. 1890.

The positioning of the mirror near the base of the barometer brought it down to a convenient standing height to be used as a mirror; this was in contrast to the convex mirrors set above the dials of many wheel barometers, with the sole purpose of being decorative and to reflect the contents of the hall or room.

The case is veneered with mahogany and the Fahrenheit mercury thermometer case is detachable. An unusual windmill scene is engraved on the brass silvered 8 inch dial and the brass acorn finial is original. The maker's name, 'J. Laffrancho, Ludlow', is engraved on the spirit level plate. He also made the normal type of Regency scroll-pediment wheel barometer and, earlier, the Sheraton shell broken-pediment barometer.

The best known of all the barometers must be the Admiral Fitzroy, which was the first cheap and serviceable barometer made by mass-production methods. An example is shown in *Fig.* 98. Identical instruments, except for variations in the pediment carving, were made in very large numbers.

It is not clear when the first Fitzroy barometer was produced, although it is claimed that it was constructed on a plan suggested by Admiral Fitzroy, but whether it was before or after he died in 1865 remains in doubt. The design does not appear to have been registered at the Patent Office, but on 11 September 1878 a J. Witherspoon registered a patent No. 3601 relating to the cases of Fitzroy barometers. He suggested that a small door be made in the side or back of the frame to enable a plug to be fixed in the cistern when the instrument is prepared for transit; the door preferably made to close against a beading to prevent dust entering the interior.

This proves that the barometer was made well before 1878 and, as it was named after the Admiral, it must be assumed that he at least inspired the maker. It could have been called Admiral Fitzroy's barometer because his words were used as weather indications on the scale and his rising and falling remarks were recorded below the scale.

Confusion could have arisen between this

barometer and the fishery or sea coast barometer already described which used Fitzroy's words on the register plates. Fitzroy was certainly responsible for having the sea coast barometer issued free by the Board of Trade and his name was associated with it.

The flat, glazed case of the Admiral Fitzroy barometer is machine-made of oak and the two pointers, which enable comparative readings to be made, can be adjusted by the two keys on the frame. A reading can be taken to one-tenth of an inch and the bulb cistern which forms the short limb has a much larger diameter than the tube to reduce the capacity error. The printed paper weather indications are those suggested by Admiral Fitzroy and immediately below these are two columns of his 'Remarks' on weather interpretation — the left-hand side for a rising barometer and the right-hand side for a falling barometer.

Rising

1st. A steady rising barometer which when continued shows very fine weather.

2nd. In Winter the rise of the barometer presages frost.

3rd. In wet weather if the mercury rise high and remain so expect fine weather but if the mercury rise suddenly very high, fine weather will not last long.

4th. A rapid rise of the barometer indicates unsettled weather, a slow movement the contrary.

N.B. The barometer rises highest of all for north and east wind.

Falling

1st. If a fall takes place with a rising thermometer wind and rain may be expected from the south-eastward, southward or south-westward.

2nd. A fall with a low thermometer foretells snow or rain.

3rd. A sudden fall of the barometer with westerly winds is generally followed by a violent storm from N.W. or N.E.

4th. A rapid fall indicates wind or wind and rain.

5th. In very hot weather the fall of the mercury denotes thunder, or a sudden fall indicates high wind.

Indications of approaching changes are shewn less by the height of the barometer than by the falling or rising. Thus the figures are of more importance than the words. The mercury falls lowest for wind and rain together, next to that for wind, except it be an east or north east wind.

Below the words on the left-hand side is a blue-coloured diagram showing the height the mercury would be in inches at any height in the atmosphere from sea level upwards in miles. This is known as the Mountain Scale and is described in detail on some Admiral Fitzroy's barometers as follows:

Air being a substance possessing gravity it necessarily presses downwards in the direction of the centre of the earth and therefore the degree of pressure on any given point will be equal to the column of air above that point and proportional to its density. The atmosphere is of the greatest vertical height at the level of the sea and here its pressure is about fifteen pounds on every square inch of surface, which pressure is exerted in every direction.

The atmosphere which envelopes the earth on every side extends to a height of about forty-five miles, deminishing in density from the sea level upwards. In the diagram is a representation of the atmosphere divided by horizontal lines into thirty spaces each containing an equal quantity of air. The lower layers however are so greatly compressed by the weight of those above them that the lower half of the atmosphere lies within four miles of the sea level, while the upper half is so much expanded as to occupy upwards of forty miles.

The following are the principal laws of air:

1st. Its pressure is equal in all directions.

2nd. Its degree of pressure depends on the vertical height and is in proportion to its density.

3rd. It affords support according to its density and to the weight of fluid displaced.

The scale on one side of the diagram indicates the height of the mercury at different elevations, thus at the top of Ben Nevis the mercury stands at about twenty-five inches, at the top of Mont Blanc about seventeen inches, and at the summit of the Himilayas, five and a half miles in altitude, at only eleven inches.

A storm-glass or chemical weather-glass is mounted over the diagram. This curious device has been in existence for more than 200 years, but the name of the inventor is unknown. Some attribute the honour to an Italian sailor, whilst others say that it was discovered by accident by some old alchemists who were constantly experimenting with the substances composing the solution with which it is made.

It is simply a glass bottle, about 10 inches long and hermetically sealed, containing crystals of potassium nitrate and ammonium chloride in an alcoholic solution of camphor with some distilled water. It was claimed to be helpful in prognosticating changes in the weather, particularly high winds, storms or tempests. In fine weather the crystals are said to settle at the bottom of the tube, while in stormy weather they are said to rise, making the solution turbid. There are certainly changes in the appearance of the solution from time to time, but they are more likely to be from variations of light and heat.

The storm-glass is really an irregular form of thermometric barometer. It must be nicely balanced as to the solubility of the camphor and salts and there are several formulas; one that is reasonably satisfactory is as follows:

Comphor	150 grains
Alcohol (90 per cent)	11 drachms
Potassium nitrate	33 grains
Ammonium chloride	38 grains
Distilled water	9 drachms

Dissolve the camphor in the alcohol and the salts in the water, then gradually add the alcoholic solution of camphor to the aqueous solution with constant shaking. The changes in the solution are said to signify the following:

Clear liquid – Bright weather.
Crystals at bottom – Thick air, frost in winter.

Fig. 99. Admiral Fitzroy's clock barometer by John G. Murdoch & Co. Ltd., c. 1895.

Dim liquid – Rain.
Dim liquid with small stars – Thunderstorms.
Large flakes – Heavy air, overcast sky, snow in
    winter.
Threads in upper portion of liquid – Windy
    weather
Small dots – Damp weather, fog.
Rising flakes which remain high – Wind in the
    upper air regions.
Small stars – In winter on bright, sunny days, snow
    in one or two days.

The higher the crystals rise in the glass tube in Winter the colder it will be. All the foregoing is empirical.

It can be seen that the Admiral Fitzroy barometer with its information on the atmosphere and short treatise on meteorology is a very interesting and collectable instrument and it is not surprising that a very large number were sold and that it remained popular until the 1930s.

Fig. 99 shows a similar barometer which was made towards the end of the nineteenth century by John G. Murdoch & Co. Ltd. of London & Melbourne. The frame is again of solid oak and the pediment has been extended to allow for an 8 day clock to be included. The printed paper backplate is more elaborately decorated and there is an additional refinement in the form of a check valve at the bottom of the bulb cistern to make it more portable. This consists of a cork attached to the end of a brass rod which is connected to a brass plate fixed to the wood base. The cork can be raised and lowered by a brass lever at the back of the barometer for the purpose of plugging the mercury in the tube whilst in transit. The lever can be locked in the lower position by applying a catch. Some check valves are made of iron. Below the printed weather information are the words 'Entered at Stationers Hall'. This relates to the hall of the 'Masters and Keepers or Wardens and Commonalty of the Mystery or Art of the Stationers of the City of London'. The Company was incorporated in 1557 and had, until the passing of the Copyright Act in 1842, an absolute monopoly as all printers were obliged to serve an apprenticeship to a member of the Company, and every publication from a bible to a ballad was required to be 'Entered at Stationers Hall'. This registration is no longer compulsory, but is still useful in making good claims of copyright.

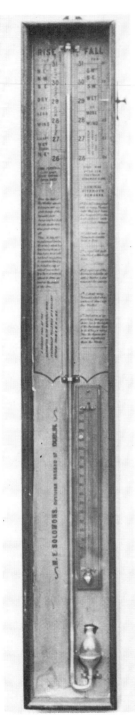

Fig. 100. Fitzroy barometer by M. E. Solomons, Dublin, c. 1900.

Fig. 101. Royal Polytechnic barometer by Joseph Davis & Co., 1880.

98

Around the turn of the century a plain and cheaper Fitzroy barometer was produced and an example is given in *Fig.* 100. It has a solid mahogany case with one brass pointer to read the scale which is compensated for capacity error. There are two columns of Admiral Fitzroy's remarks on weather interpretation, but a storm-glass is not fitted. The usual Fahrenheit mercury thermometer is mounted on a boxwood scale and the maker's name, 'M. E. Solomons, Optician, Nassau St., Dublin', is printed opposite the thermometer. This type of barometer is still easily obtainable and instruments can be found with a selection of words used from Admiral Fitzroy's remarks; some have storm-glasses fitted.

Mention should be made of the interesting and distinctive bulb cistern barometer known as the Royal Polytechnic barometer and shown in *Fig.* 101. The sole manufacturer in England was Joseph Davis & Co., Royal Polytechnic Institution, Kennington Park Rd., London who produced them between 1870 and 1885. They were also made under licence in various other countries.

The glazed case is made of oak and everything about the barometer is symmetrical, except for the tube. A Fahrenheit and a centigrade thermometer are fitted below two columns of Admiral Fitzroy's special remarks for rising and falling conditions and these are similar to the words on the Admiral Fitzroy barometers already illustrated. The two ivory keys, below the circular dial, control pointers each side of the tube to which are attached hands that indicate the weather conditions listed round the dial. These cover seven winter and eight summer possible weather combinations from 'Very fine with frost' to 'Very stormy with heavy gales'. The action of setting the pointer against the level of the mercury automatically moves the hand to one of the weather signs which predicts the approaching weather. There are two sets of pointers and hands so that daily comparisons of the readings can be made.

Some of these barometers have enclosed cases with a single thermometer and some have seven small segment dials, set below the main dial, so that daily readings can be recorded for a week at a time.

The school laboratory siphon tube barometer shown in *Fig.* 102 cannot be classed as an antique as it was probably made in the twentieth century. It is suggested that it was made for use by school pupils, in science and chemistry laboratories, solely for the purpose of measuring atmospheric pressures. The tube is of the same bore throughout its length and the boxwood scale is calibrated in centimetres and millimetres from zero to 80 centimetres. Before taking a reading the zero on the scale is set in line with the mercury in the short limb by turning the screw on the right-hand side of the frame. The mercury thermometer has its Fahrenheit paper scale contained within a sealed tube. This

Fig. 102. School laboratory siphon tube barometer, c. 1920.

type of thermometer will float upright in a liquid and it was probably detached from time to time and used to take the temperature of liquids in various apparatus.

7 Aneroid Barometers

It was the invention of the compact and truly portable aneroid barometer by Lucien Vidie in 1843 that heralded the virtual demise of the relatively expensive but elegant mercury barometer.

Lucien Vidie was born at Nantes in France in 1805 and intended to become a lawyer. However, he was by nature shy, sensitive and retiring and in 1830 he came to the conclusion that he was not really suited to this profession and he left it to take up steam engineering. At that time a column of mercury was an essential part of a steam pressure gauge and he began research with the object of improving its efficiency.

This led him to an interest in mercury barometers, and in 1843 he succeeded in producing a metallic barometer called an 'aneroid' which means without liquid. It consisted of a shallow, sealed metallic chamber, almost exhausted of air, with its upper and lower surfaces corrugated in concentric circles to make them flexible. The lower surface was fixed and the sides of the chamber were prevented from collapsing inwards by internal springs. The upper surface was in contact with the short arm of a lever and a longer arm operated an index pointer. Changes of atmospheric pressure caused changes in the height of the chamber and so moved the index pointer which was magnified by the lever system.

An idea of the construction can be gained from *Fig.* 103 which shows a modern aneroid barometer so constructed that the scale and the interior can be seen at the same time.

Before taking out a patent in England in 1844 Vidie arranged for Andrew Pritchard, a London manufacturing optician, to make and test the barometer. This he did from the drawings and specifications supplied by Vidie and he tested it to his satisfaction, which included taking it up to the dome of St Paul's Cathedral to check height and pressure change.

A series of observations were carried out in 1848; during March simultaneous readings from an aneroid and a mercurial barometer were recorded and were found to be almost identical. Similar experiments were carried out in the winter of 1849 with corresponding results. To establish the portability of the aneroid for measuring heights and to show its convenience as a meteorological barometer, a series of observations were made during a train journey from London to Chester in 1848, and again in 1848 on the Caledonian Railway between Preston and Carlisle. As the movement of the aneroid was found to be always consistent it was suggested that the tourist should never be without one and that seamen would find it a safe guide when the motion of the mercurial column renders the marine barometer almost useless.

Vidie had difficulty in selling his new barometer in France, but he was more successful in England. He exhibited it in 1851 at the Great Exhibition in London, where he was awarded a Council Medal. Bourdon, a Paris instrument maker, also exhibited a similar type of aneroid barometer and Vidie sued him for infringement of the patent. He lost the case – and an appeal – but renewed his fight later and was

Fig. 103. Modern aneroid barometer.

Fig. 104. Marine aneroid barometer by Manning & Co., c. 1860.

awarded damages of 10,000 Francs in 1861.

Little is known of the development of the aneroid barometer during the 1850s, except that various improvements were made to the internal spiral spring, with some being fitted with an external spring, and the construction generally became more sophisticated. Thought was also given to corrections in the readings required owing to changes in temperature, and two systems were adopted. The first involved the use of a bimetallic link in the mechanism, using a combination of brass and steel, and the second system was to leave a small quantity of air or gas in the metallic chamber; both would compensate for the effects of heat and cold on the chamber.

The early aneroid barometers made around 1860 in commercial quantities usually had card or silvered metal dials with a diameter of 4½ inches. Instruments specially adapted for use at sea were usually fitted with enamel dials as the porcelain surface was less likely to corrode. The mechanism was housed in a brass cylindrical case with a depth of about 2 inches. The dial was similar to that of a wheel barometer with a 3 inch scale from 28 to 31 inches graduated in tenths and fiftieths of an inch. Weather indications were generally Stormy, Rain, Change, Fair and Very Dry. The dial was protected by glass with a brass set hand operated by a knob through the centre. A blued steel indicating hand was used.

Fig. 104 shows an example by Manning & Company of Worcester, with a card dial, made for marine use. It has the additional weather signs of West or More Wind, Dry or Less Wind, Fall for S. Wly., S.E., S.W. and Rise for N. Ely., N.W., N.E. It also has a mercury Fahrenheit curved thermometer with the bulb positioned under the dial so that it can more accurately record the temperature of the metal chamber. There is a screw at the back of the case to move the indicating hand when setting up the barometer and for subsequent adjustment, if found necessary.

Similar barometers were made from around 1860 to measure altitudes; these were fitted with a revolving ring with a range of scale up to 20,000 feet and a magnifier was included. The scale was in feet and was calibrated on the dial in an anti-clockwise direction. To use the instrument as an altimeter the scale zero was set adjacent to the indicating hand, so that when the barometer was taken up an incline the hand would move backwards. As the barometer falls more or less progressively one-tenth of an inch for every 90 feet it is taken above sea level, it is easy to calculate the height at any time. To obtain an accurate measurement two people should take simultaneous readings from two barometers, one being at the bottom and the other at the top of the incline being measured.

Although aneroid barometers will operate satisfactorily face upwards on a flat surface, they are intended to be suspended with the dial vertical, and each is fitted with a hanging ring. They are set by the makers in a vertical position and the reading will differ by a few hundredths of an inch if taken when in a horizontal position.

Vidie's patents expired in 1859 and Admiral Fitzroy, realising that the aneroid barometer could be of great benefit to sailors, travellers and mountaineers because of its portability, persuaded Messrs Negretti & Zambra to reduce its size so that it could be carried in the pocket. He also suggested improving its mechanical arrangement and compensation for temperature.

The firm undertook research and in 1860 succeeded in producing a pocket aneroid barometer with an overall diameter of 2¾ inches and a depth of 1 inch. The compensation was carefully adjusted and the scale, which extended from 31 to 23 inches, was graduated under reduced pressure so that the dimensions were not quite equal, but more accurate.

Barometers of similar size and design were also made with an additional scale for measuring altitudes, and an example is shown in *Fig.* 105, complete with silk-lined leather-covered case. The silvered metal scale extends from 31 to 18 inches and the altitude range is to 15,000 feet. The weather indications are reduced to Rain, Change and Fair and the instrument is shown to be Compensated. There is no recording hand as it has been replaced by a fine pointer attached to a milled brass rim which can be adjusted by rotating the rim round the dial manually.

Similar instruments were also made to measure altitudes up to 10,000 and 20,000 feet, complete in a leather case as shown. Tables were also provided so that the height above sea level could be easily calculated at any time.

Negretti & Zambra continued to develop these barometers and in 1861 marketed watch-sized aneroid barometers in gilt metal cases. These were less than 2 inches in diameter with a depth of little more than half an inch. They also offered similar size instruments for meteorological observations or altitude measurements to 10,000 and 20,000 feet. These barometers were also advertised in stout silver cases or solid gold highly-finished cases. They could be purchased from opticians in silver shut-up cases very similar to the hunter watch. Table stands for all aneroid barometers, of carved oak or other woods, were also produced with ships aneroid barometers in suitable mountings.

A typical watch-sized aneroid or mountain aneroid barometer is shown in *Fig.* 106. It is very like the Negretti & Zambra barometers just described, but was made a little later. It has a diameter of 1¾ inches and a depth of five-eighths of an inch. The silvered metal scale covers 8 inches so that heights up to 8,000 feet can be measured on the outer scale, which has a graduation for each 100 feet. The barometer scale is divided into tenths and twentieths of an inch. Rain, Change and Fair are engraved on the dial with the makers name, 'Chadburns Ltd. Liverpool'. It was made around 1870. There is no need for a recording or set pointer as the height scale can be rotated manually round the barometer scale. The Chadburn family made and sold barometers and optical and mathematical instruments in Sheffield and Liverpool from the beginning of the nineteenth century.

Fig. 107 shows a pocket watch-sized aneroid of similar size in a silk-lined leather-covered case. The barometer case is again of brass and the scale covers 10 inches divided into twentieths of an inch. Heights of up to 10,000 feet can be measured with the divisions covering 50 feet. Rain, Change and Fair together with Compensated are engraved on the silvered metal dial. The recording system is more sophisticated than that used on the earlier barometers and consists of a stem wind adjustment; by turning the stem winder the outer altitude scale is rotated so that zero can be set in any position on the barometer scale. There is a dial hand adjustment screw at the back of the case. The barometer was made about 1875. Quite a number of pocket watch-sized barometers made at this time had a curved Fahrenheit mercury thermometer fitted to the lower half of the scale, whilst some had a small magnetic compass built into the back of the case as an aid to travellers. The compass could affect the barometer reading or vice versa, and to avoid this it was recommended that, before taking a reading or consulting the compass, the barometer be turned so that the indicating pointer was in line with the North and South; this neutralised the interaction between the steel arbor and the magnetised needle.

Over the years various other improvements were made to the aneroid barometer

Fig. 105. Pocket aneroid barometer in leather case, c. 1865.

Fig. 106. Watch-size aneroid barometer by Chadburns Ltd., Liverpool, c. 1870.

Fig. 107. Stem wind watch-size aneroid barometer, c. 1875.

Fig. 108. Pocket aneroid barometer in standing case, c. 1885.

Fig. 109. Watch-size aneroid barometer by Negretti & Zambra, c. 191

In 1861 James Pitkin, a notable maker, used jewels in his movements and was granted a patent. Attempts were made to improve the vacuum chamber, with copper, brass and, later, nickel alloys being used; flat external springs were tried with multiple chambers and, later, Negretti & Zambra used an internal leaf spring in each chamber; this system was used until well into the twentieth century.

In the National Maritime Museum, Greenwich, there is a miniature aneroid barometer with a case of chased gold, with a diameter of only seven-eighths of an inch.

By 1850 most opticians carried a stock of pocket or mountain aneroid barometers with diameters ranging from 1¼ inches to 3¾ inches, and they were made until the beginning of the twentieth century. They were popular with travellers and used by climbers to measure the height of mountains. Miners also used them to establish the depth of mines.

A pocket aneroid barometer made towards the end of the nineteenth century is illustrated in *Fig.* 108. It has a silvered case with an enamel dial and a blued steel indicating hand. The set pointer is attached to a milled rim and can be rotated round the dial by hand. Five standard weather indications are used, and as the scale extends down to 26 inches it was obviously made to be used by a traveller, although it is housed in a standing leather case. The case is lined with a rich blue velvet and originally had a carrying or hanging strap attached to each side. It was made around 1885.

A very interesting and intricate watch-sized aneroid barometer is illustrated in *Fig.* 109. It was patented by Negretti & Zambra in 1915 and has three separate adjustment mechanisms to ensure that the weather can be forecast accurately.

It is a traveller's barometer and has an 'Altitude in Feet' scale from zero to 3,000 round the side of the case, and the indicating pointer is adjusted for height by rotating the milled rim at the back of the case. Allowance can be made for the direction of the wind by rotating the milled rim at the front of the case and this rotates three concentric circles of letters of the alphabet under the metal disc which covers the central half of the dial. The letters can be seen through the three apertures marked Fall, Rise and Steady in the central disc. The third adjustment necessary before reading the barometer is to turn the stem wind mechanism until zero on the central disc is in line with the indicating pointer. One of the three

106

letters then appearing through the apertures is selected depending on whether the previous reading shows the barometer to be falling, rising or steady. The back of the case is divided into 26 segments each engraved with a letter of the alphabet and an individual weather forecast ranging from 'A = Settled Fine' to 'Z = Stormy. Much Rain'. From the letter selected the appropriate forecast can be obtained.

Opticians also stocked marine or yachting barometers in 1850. These could be obtained in three sizes; 4½ inches, 6 inches and 8 inches in diameter and were suitable for use by mariners because of the clear lettering and figuring on their dials. The dials were made of cardboard, enamel or metal. Cardboard dials were used on the cheapest barometers; they were mass produced and so considered not as accurate as the metal dials where the scales were divided specially for each barometer. Enamel dials were considered the best for marine use because the porcelain surface would not corrode. These barometers were produced with 'closed' or 'open' dials. The aneroids already described all have closed dials and an example of a 6 inch open dial marine barometer can be seen in *Fig.* 110. There is no operational difference between the two types, but the open dial is the more interesting as the majority of the movement can be easily seen. The barometer is housed in a brass case with a silvered brass dial. The scale is calibrated in fiftieths of an inch and the movement is compensated for changes in temperature. Two curved thermometers are housed on the dial; the one on the left is filled with alcohol and carries centigrade and Reaumur scales, whilst the one on the right is filled with mercury and has a Fahrenheit scale. The dial is engraved 'Salom and Co. Makers' and it was probably made around 1875. This type of barometer is difficult to date accurately as they were made over a period of more than 50 years with no material alterations.

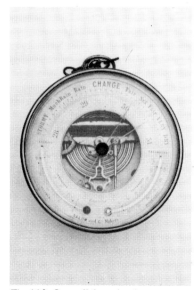

Fig. 110. Open dial marine barometer by Salom & Co., c. 1875.

Fig. 111. Oak ship's barometer, c. 1885.

Another very popular type of marine or ship's aneroid barometer which was made from 1850 for at least half a century is shown in *Fig.* 111. The case is of solid oak and is carved to simulate a twisted rope surround. The 6 inch porcelain dial has a black painted scale and the usual weather indications are elaborately and attractively drawn with the capital letters picked out in red. It has additional weather signs which are usually included on marine barometers.

By the second half of the nineteenth century the aneroid barometer was firmly established as a reliable weather indicator, although it was still recommended to compare it at intervals of 12 months with a standard mercurial barometer and, if necessary, adjust it by means of the screw set in the back of all aneroid barometers. Opticians would usually keep a mercurial barometer for this purpose; they also sold notebooks, complete with pencil and india-rubber, called a 'Pocket Meteorological Register and Note-Book' so that diagrams could be completed showing the fluctuations of the barometer from day to day. Admiral Fitzroy prepared an explanatory card and suggested the sale of the notebook.

As has already been intimated, the marine barometer continued to be made in the twentieth century, and one sold by John Barker & Co. Ltd. of Kensington, London, is shown in *Fig.* 112. It was made in the 1920s and shows little change from the barometer just described, other than being more austere. There is a greater depth of brass and the moulded base is of solid oak.

Circular aneroid barometers of larger diameters were also made from around 1850. Those with dials of 10, 14 and 16 inches were usually found on the walls of public halls and counting houses, whilst the coastguard or factory aneroids were made with dials varying between 18 and 24 inches. These larger barometers were usually made to order as they did not form part of the opticians general stock.

Until the second half of the nineteenth century the appeal of the aneroid barometer was mainly limited to engineers, surveyors and scientific observers, who used them for taking altitude measurements, and mining engineers, who used them extensively for calculating depths below ground. They were also purchased by government departments, for issue to army and navy personnel, whilst travellers, mariners and tourists appreciated their portability.

Round brass-cased aneroid barometers were, by this time, made for the home, with some being incorporated in marble statuettes or sculptured groups of figures as ornaments for the Victorian mantelpiece or for hanging in the hall or library. A popular arrangement of barometer, clock and thermometer set in an ornamental ebonised wood mounting is shown in *Fig.* 113. It was made by Negretti and Zambra around 1870 and is 7½ inches in height. The 8 day clock has a vertical platform cylinder escapement and the thermometer has a Fahrenheit scale. The clock and barometer dials are enamelled whilst the thermometer scale is made of ivory. The mounting for this type of barometer was sometimes made with a cast metal.

In an endeavour to popularise the aneroid as a domestic barometer some makers began, around 1850, to house them in cases very similar to those used for wheel mercurial barometers. The design was quickly accepted and it was not long before a large number of aneroid barometers were produced and sold with moulded and carved oak cases similar to the wheel barometers shown in *Figs.* 83, 84 and 85. A very large number and variety was made during the second half of the nineteenth century, with some appearing identical to the banjo type; in fact, it is sometimes necessary to look at the back of the case to see whether a door or a screw is fitted before being sure whether the case houses a mercurial or aneroid

Fig. 112. Oak ship's barometer, c. 1920.

Fig. 113. Clock barometer by Negretti & Zambra, c. 1870.

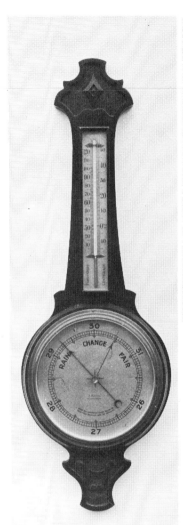

Fig. 115. Mahogany aneroid barometer, c. 1890.

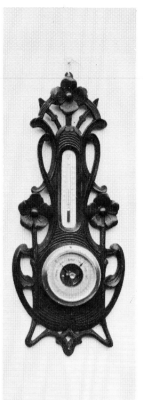

Fig. 116. Art nouveau period barometer c. 1905.

Fig. 114. Mahogany aneroid barometer, c. 1910.

barometer. A thermometer was always fitted above the dial and occasionally a clock was incorporated in the pediment.

Later barometers were made to similar designs, resembling the external appearance of the wheel barometer, except that they were smaller in size. Fig. 114 shows a typical aneroid barometer made at the beginning of the twentieth century. It has a solid mahogany case with a detachable mercury thermometer with Fahrenheit and centigrade scales. The overall height is 29 inches. The dials are of silvered brass and the name of the retailer, F. Hilser, Trowbridge, is engraved on the lower half of the main dial. Frank Hilser was a jeweller who owned a shop in Fore Street, Trowbridge, from the beginning of the twentieth century. At that time barometers could be purchased from most jewellers, opticians and instrument retailers.

The most popular late Victorian aneroid is illustrated in *Fig.* 115. The case is of mahogany with a height of only 18 inches, including the finials. The open porcelain dial is elegantly painted with the first letter of each weather indication coloured red. The thermometer·is not protected by glass and carries the two usual scales. Barometers of this design were made in very large numbers between 1880 and 1905.

An interesting barometer of the art nouveau period is shown in *Fig.* 116. Its overall height is 18 inches and the open dial is similar to the last one described, except that it is painted to simulate silver with black and red lettering. The frame is elegantly carved and fretted with leaves, stems and flowers.

In 1914 E. Gold of the Meteorological Office, London, suggested the millibar as a unit of atmospheric pressure. It was adopted by the Meteorological Office and introduced as the unit of pressure in the daily weather reports from 1 April 1914. A Meteorological Office aneroid barometer Mark I is shown in *Fig.* 117. It was designed by the Meteorological Office in 1919 and is compensated for change of temperature. In addition to the scale of pressure in inches of mercury there is also a millibar scale. The initials 'M. O.' on the dial indicate that it was made for the Meteorological Office by Short and Mason of London around 1920. Mark I is engraved on the back of the brass case; a Mark II barometer was introduced later when the scale of pressure in inches of mercury was omitted. These barometers were used in weather stations and on board ships.

Fig. 117. Meteorological Office barometer Mark I by Short & Mason, London, c. 1920.

The aneroid barometer continued to be popular and instruments similar to those shown in *Figs.* 104, 110 and 112 are still made today.

A review of barometers would not be complete without referring to the recording barometer or barograph, which still has a strong appeal to the amateur weather forecaster.

The first recording meteorological instrument was made by Christopher Wren in 1663 and called a weather clock; it was improved by Robert Hooke who made use of the siphon cistern principle, as in a wheel barometer. Very few mercury barographs were produced, but one or two are on view in the Science Museum, London. The same does not apply to the aneroid barograph, which was produced from around 1865 and remained popular until well into the twentieth century.

An example of the aneroid barograph is shown in *Fig.* 118. It operates on the same principle as the aneroid barometer in that the expansion and contraction of a series of partially exhausted boxes are transmitted by levers to a pointer. The pointer has a pen attachment which moves over a chart wound round a drum which, activated by clockwork, rotates round its vertical axis once every 7 days. The pen leaves behind it a continuous visual record of all pressure changes and the trend shown is of great assistance when forecasting weather changes. The record so produced is called a barogram. The barogram is traced on a kind of graph paper

Fig. 118. Oak barograph, c. 1920.

which is divided lengthwise into the 7 days of the week, with each division representing 2 hours; the heavy vertical lines are at midday and midnight. The pressure scale is from 28 to 31 inches with divisions of one-tenth of an inch. The clockwork has an 8 day movement and is wound up by removing the top of the drum which exposes the winding key and adjustment lever. It is essential to wind the clock mechanism and change the paper scale each Monday before midday to prevent the pen from passing over the brass bar which retains the scale in position; if this happens the pen could be damaged or require adjustment on the arm.

The barograph is a delicate instrument and needs to be handled carefully, particularly when refilling the pen with ink, removing the drum to fit a fresh paper or winding the clock mechanism. The stand is made of oak, with a drawer to keep a supply of paper scales, and the glass top can be lifted off to allow the weekly servicing. There is an adjustable bar to hold the pen away from the drum before removing it and also a screw to set and adjust the height of the recording arm.

A special purple ink is used and some barographs have a container for the ink bottle within the case. Others are fitted with a thermometer, whilst a few have, as an addition, a dial and indicating hand similar to that used on the dial of an aneroid barometer.

8 Care of barometers

It is probably true to say that one of the most important things to know about barometers is how to handle them. Aneroid barometers are reasonably robust, but mercurial barometers, particularly those with open cisterns, must be handled with great care or the mercury in the tube may be so displaced that it becomes necessary to refill the tube. This can only be undertaken by a specialist restorer who has the equipment to evacuate the tube.

The most delicate barometer is the early cistern tube barometer with an open cistern, as illustrated in *Fig.* 2. It must be kept in a vertical or near vertical position and not be subjected to any abrupt movement whatsoever, as this could well result in a loss of mercury in the cistern and, possibly, air bubbles in the tube. A lowering of the level of mercury in the cistern will distort the barometer reading as it will record a lower figure, but this can be corrected by topping up the mercury in the cistern using another barometer for comparison.

To get rid of the air bubbles in the tube it is necessary to remove the tube from the cistern, after plugging the open end with a finger, and then invert it. By gently shaking the tube it should be possible to eliminate the bubbles; the mercury should then be topped up in the tube which can then be returned to the cistern.

Before any stick barometer is transported it is advisable to remove the cistern cover in order to determine the type of cistern used. Closed cistern tube barometers are less vulnerable to damage, as the mercury cannot be spilt unless there is a fissure between the tube and the boxwood cistern or a split has occurred in the leather base of the boxwood cistern; in either case the repair should be carried out by a professional restorer.

Almost all closed cistern barometers are fitted with portable screws, which have already been described in Chapter 2. Before transit the screw should always be applied so that all the air is removed from the cistern and the tube is completely full of mercury. It is preferable to incline the barometer at an angle of 45 degrees before turning the screw, as this will allow the mercury to rise freely to the top of the tube and reduce the pressure on the screw whilst being turned. The barometer can then be carried or rested in any position.

Closed cistern tube barometers without portable screws should be carried at an angle of 45 degrees so that the mercury is always at the top of the tube; this prevents the mercury from rising and falling in the tube whilst in motion and stops air bubbles gaining access to the tube. If the mercury is allowed to rise too sharply in the tube its force against the top of the tube can break the glass.

Bulb cistern stick barometers can be carried carefully at an angle of 45 degrees, but they should never be laid flat as mercury will spill from the bulb cistern and air bubbles may appear in the tube. The mercury lost from the cistern can be replaced, but it is difficult to remove the air bubbles and the tube will most probably have to be refilled. When this type of barometer has to be moved any great distance it is advisable to plug the tube. The plug consists of a short piece of wire with wool wound round one end and a movable cork at the other. Before plugging the tube the barometer should be inclined so that the mercury rises to the top of the tube; the wool end of the wire is then forced into the tube where the bore narrows near the bend and is kept in this position by sliding the cork down the wire until it is firmly fixed into the opening of the bulb cistern. The wool prevents the mercury in the tube from returning to the cistern whilst the cork prevents the mercury in the cistern from escaping. With the plug firmly in position the barometer can be carried or positioned at any angle.

All wheel barometers are fitted with siphon tubes, and when it is necessary to move them the precautions outlined for bulb cistern stick barometers should be followed. As the short limb of a siphon tube is much longer than that of a bulb cistern tube it will be necessary to use a longer wire for the plug, but the instructions for fitting it still apply. The glass weight resting on the mercury should be removed from the tube before the plug is fixed and it is advisable to pin or Sellotape both silk threads to the frame just below the pulley to ensure that they stay in their respective grooves on the pulley.

To reset the barometer it should be held at an angle of 45 degrees; first extract the plug from the tube and lower the weight on to the mercury; then remove the pin or Sellotape holding the silk threads, taking care to keep the silks taut meanwhile. On reverting·to an upright position the barometer should again be in working order and still accurate.

If it is found, by comparison or otherwise, that a cistern tube barometer is not recording a correct reading, the mercury should first be examined. If there are no air bubbles present, which are evidenced by breaks in the mercury, the tube should be inclined to one side – gradually at first – to see whether the mercury rises to the top of the tube with a dull thud which vibrates the tube. If this happens it can be assumed that there is a good vacuum, but if there is no thud or the mercury fails to reach the top of the tube, it indicates that air has penetrated the vacuum and the tube should be replaced. If the tube is functioning correctly the reading can be adjusted by raising or lowering the tube by adding to or removing some of the packing in the cistern housing. On some barometers it is possible to raise or lower the register plates.

With bulb cistern barometers there is a further adjustment which can be made by raising or lowering the mercury in the bulb cistern.

There are several ways of adjusting the reading of a wheel barometer and these include raising or lowering the tube, altering the level of the mercury in the short tube or adjusting the length of the silk thread. All three are difficult operations and the easiest method is to remove the dial bezel and adjust the indicating hand; this is best achieved by holding the pulley firmly with one hand and easing the set hand round the spindle with the other. The barometer must, of course, be held in a vertical position during the adjustment.

Great care should be taken when using mercury as it is poisonous. It is sensible to wash your hands after using it and it should not be left exposed to vaporise. It does not affect wood, but it is advisable to recover any mercury that has been spilt in the workshop and to keep it in a closed container.

The general restoration of barometers is outside the scope of this book, but the care of the various silvered dials and register plates should be mentioned.

Silvering that is discoloured may be restored satisfactorily by brushing with cream of tartar and water on a very soft brush. It will have no effect on the waxed lettering, but may wash off any painted letters. If this does not bring back the surface to an acceptable standard the dial should be resilvered.

There are various formulae for silvering compounds and diverse methods of application, but the following compound and method has proved to be satisfactory. Prepare a mixture of 3 parts silver chloride, 20 parts cream of tartar and 15 parts sodium chloride. Remove the existing silver with a very fine emery cloth or other light abrasive until it has been completely removed and the brass fully exposed. Polish the brass with a clean rag and rub again with tissue paper until it is absolutely clean; the brass should rest on a clean surface and should not be touched by hand. Mix the compound with water until a liquid paste is formed and then rub on to the brass with a cotton wool swab using a circular motion; change the swab frequently — it may be found preferable to use each swab only once. When the brass is covered with silver, rinse it under a cold tap and dry gently in a clean cloth and then air dry. If the resilvering is then lacquered it will remain in excellent condition for a very long time.

Some restorers prefer to resilver the main wheel barometer dial when it is revolving on a turntable as this method produces silvering which appears to be made up of innumerable concentric circles across the face of the dial.

A problem arises if the silk thread attached to the glass weight, or to the glass counterpoise weight, becomes dislodged from the pulley grooves, as it is very difficult to replace them once they become entwined round the pulley spindle. It may be possible, given time and patience, to return them to the pulley, but the quickest and least frustrating way is to remove the dial bezel and indicating hand; then unscrew the screw holding the pulley support so that the pulley can be removed. It will then be an easy operation to replace the silk on the pulley and reset the barometer as already described.

The various screws used in the construction of barometers can sometimes be difficult to remove, particularly those that were produced before 1851 when all wood screws were made by hand; these screws can easily be distinguished because of their blunt ends. To avoid damaging the brass plates by leverage, it may be possible to loosen a screw by applying paraffin or penetrating oil to the head; an alternative is to place a screwdriver in the head slot and strike the screwdriver with a mallet. Only as a last resort should a red hot poker be applied to the head of the screw or the head be drilled away with a hand drill.

Dirty ivory register plates and thermometer scales can be cleaned by using the finest flour paper and polished with methylated spirits and whiting.

In contrast with the mercurial barometer the aneroid barometer can be moved and transported without difficulty; if handled with reasonable care it is unlikely to need any attention save, perhaps, for adjustment of the indicating hand if it is not reading correctly. This can be easily achieved by using a screwdriver to turn the set screw, visible through a small aperture at the back of the case, until the hand points to the correct reading.

Aneroid barometers are always set to give a correct reading in an upright or hanging position, and a slightly different reading will be obtained if taken when the barometer is face upwards.

One final point, always tap the barometer glass before reading.

Bibliography

Adams, George (1790) — *A Short Dissertation on the Barometer, Thermometer and other Meteorological Instruments*. London.

Baillie, G. H. (1951) — *Watchmakers and Clockmakers of the World*, 3rd ed. N.A.G. Press, London.

Bell, G. H. and Bell, E. F. (1952) — *Old English Barometers*. The Wykeham Press, Winchester.

Bellchambers, J. K. (1968) — *Somerset Clockmakers*. Antiquarian Horological Society, London.

Belville, J. H. (1849) — *A Manual of the Barometer*. London.

Britten, F. J. (1922) — *Old Watches and Clocks and their Makers*, 5th ed. London.

Fellow of the Meteorological Society (1849) — *The Aneroid Barometer, How to Buy and Use It*. London.

Goodison, N. (1969) — *English Barometers and their Makers 1680–1860*. London, Cassell.

Middleton, W. E. K. (1964) — *The History of the Barometer*. The John Hopkins Press, Baltimore.

Negretti & Zambra (1864) — *A Treatise on Meteorological Instruments*. London.

Rees, Abraham (1819) — *The Cyclopaedia*. London.

Saul, Edward (1735) — *A Historical and Philosophical Account of the Barometer*. London.